Please note the information contained within this document is for educational and entertainment purposes only. All effort has been executed to present accurate, up to date, reliable, complete information. No warranties of any kind are declared or implied. Readers acknowledge that the author is not engaged in the rendering of legal, financial, medical, or professional advice. The content within this book has been derived from various sources. Please consult a licensed professional before attempting any techniques outlined in this book. By reading this document, the reader agrees that under no circumstances is the author responsible for any losses, direct or indirect, that are incurred as a result of the use of the information contained within this document, including, but not limited to, errors, omissions, or inaccuracies.

CONTENTS

INTRODUCTION

Welcome to Whole30 Program and healthier and well balanced life! In this book you will find everything you need to know about Whole30 diet so you would be able to start off with your new healthier lifestyle. Besides from basic and detailed info on Whole30 program, you will also find 84 recipes, divided in four categories: breakfast, lunch, dinner and snack recipes, along with a 14-day meal program that is assembled to help you start off the right foot from day number one!

Welcome and enjoy cooking with whole food and fresh ingredients!

CHAPTER 1: WHAT IS WHOLE30 PROGRAM?

Everything You Need To Know About Whole30 Diet

In all the rush and hurry in our everyday lives and problems, we often stop paying attention to what we are introducing our body to when we eat. That is usually the case until you feel that you are not content with how your body works: you start noticing that you have gained weight, there are chronic pains and problems with digestion appearing without any known or logical reasons. You might also notice that you are having seasonal allergies and other physical and health problems, like inability to lose extra weight you are having problems with. The first logical action to neutralize these problems is to go and see a doctor, who will by all means prescribe medications. But what happens when those medications turn out to be useless with solving your problems?

A lot of people out there don't understand that the phrase: "You are what you eat." Is more than just a phrase. Due to inconsistent and malnutrition your body may respond with pain, chronic gastro problems, allergies and even more severe problems like diabetes, heart problems, blood pressure issues, obesity and different types of inflammation. The main catch about food besides from giving you pleasure – the brain produces serotonin, happiness hormone, whenever you eat – food is supposed to give you energy, make you healthy and feeling refreshed and ready for action. You have surely noticed that sometimes, even though you have eaten well, you feel a lack of energy that is setting you back. That is because some types of food are simply not made for you. Specifically, in the spirit of Whole30 program, we are addressing legumes, sugar, dairy and grains as a massive and definite NO. No matter how tasty these types of food can be prepared, you should by all means expel them from your diet when entering a Whole30 diet plan and a great plus, you will feel better and look in accordance with how you feel. To introduce you to the rules of Whole30 program, we will explain in detail which food types are good for you and which types of food you should avoid by all means.

Whole30 Program DON'T's

These types of food should be avoided at all costs when following up with Whole30 program that is especially designed to help you cleanse your body, make your body healthier, lose excessive weight that is getting in your way of feeling great and solve physical and health problems like obesity, high blood pressure, prevent diabetes and lower blood sugar in your body as well as prevent heart diseases and different types of inflammation. Remember: You ARE what you eat.

Sugar

In Whole30 program there is no room for sugar. Sugar represents empty carbs so your body is n it getting any of the nutrients it needs – the only thing you can get with consuming sugar is diabetes, increased levels of sugar in your blood that could lead to diabetes and extra weight you don't want or need. Food companies tend to add sugar even in the most unexpected foods, so always make sure you check the label before making a purchase. In Whole30 program, added sugar is not allowed – whether we are talking about artificial or natural sugar. You are not allowed to consume maple syrup, stevia, coconut sugar, xylitol, agave nectar, dates syrup, honey or any other type of sugar.

Grains

You shouldn't eat any type of grains and this will include rice, quinoa, barley, starch, bran, corn, wheat, oats, bulgur, buckwheat, sprouted grains of any type, amaranth, sorghum or any other type of grains or gluten-free grains. Regardless of the absence of gluten in some types of grains like amaranth or quinoa, you shouldn't use any grains in your diet.

Alcohol

Many of you surely have a habit of cooking with alcohol like sherry or wine, or simple drinking a glass of wine with your dinner, but if you are planning on going Whole30 and improve your overall health and quality of your life, you should avoid alcohol consumption in any form.

Legumes

You are not allowed to eat any type of legumes as legumes are not in accordance with policy of Whole30 program. Soy would be strictly prohibited as well as soy foods like tofu, soy sauce, tempeh or added soy derivates like lecithin. Lecithin is often added to processed food, so always make sure to check your labels whenever you are in doubt, just for the sake of precaution. Also, legumes would include any type of beans: so, no lima beans, kidney beans, red or white beans, or any type of beans allowed. You will also avoid lentils, peas, peanuts and chickpeas. Peanuts "prohibition" would also include foods containing traces of peanuts as well as peanut butter.

Dairy Products

Any type of dairy product is not allowed, which would include milk (cow, goat or sheep milk), yogurt, any other types of yogurt like kefir, cheese, cream cheese or ice cream with milk (basically every ice cream there is – except from vegan ice creams that contain no dairy products – but those would also be a bog NO in case of added sugar)

Processed food

Any processed food containing sulfites, carrageenan or MSG. Always check the labels on the processed foods you are planning on consuming in order to avoid purchasing and consumption of these additives.

Junk Foods

Junk food is out of any question if you are planning on developing healthier habits, so say no to all types of junk food.

Baked Foods

Foods like cupcakes, pancakes, bread, biscuits, muffins, cookies, pizza, brownies, tortillas, chips, waffles, French fries – anything of that type or similar to these foods should be avoided when on Whole30. Anything you believe would make a rule breaking snack or lunch should be avoided. If you are in doubt whether something can pass as Whole30 or not, you should check it and make sure (100%) that it is allowed in your diet and if not just say no and switch it for something that is allowed under Whole30 program.

Exceptions

Exception confirms the rule, right? So, there are a couple of exceptions that you could use in your Whole30 program. You will find the list below.

The only allowed source of dairy

The only dairy source allowed during Whole30 would be ghee and clarified butter. In case you didn't know, ghee is avocado butter and is great for cooking.

Juiced Fruit

Homemade unsweetened fruit juice will come in as handy for some recipes and you can also drink it. It can be used in some recipes as a substitute for sugar. However, you are not allowed to add sugar, artificial or natural, to your fruit juice.

Exceptions for some Legumes

Although legumes are strictly prohibited, some legumes are allowed and encouraged for using in your Whole30 program. The legumes you can use are green beans, snow peas and sugar snap peas. These are very close to greens based on their composition, so you are allowed to use these legumes.

Vinegar

You can use all types of vinegar during Whole30, with only one exception: malt vinegar because it contains gluten. You can use apple cider vinegar, wine vinegar, white vinegar, rice vinegar, balsamic vinegar and similar vinegars to those.

Coconut aminos

You might have heard about this marvelous condiment – it is actually a substitute for soy sauce and goes great with many different dishes. Make sure you buy this amazing nectar as it's useful to have it around your kitchen.

Salt

You can use salt, kosher or sea salt – and although salt contains sugar which prevents the salt from losing ions, salt is still allowed within Whole30 diet.

Whole30 Program DO's

Although you might think that the list of DON'T's is quite longish, we are presenting a list of foods you are allowed to eat during the Whole30 program – you will see that there is a lot of possibilities for preparing different tasty and healthy meals that will help you with leading a healthier life.

Minimally processed food

Whole30 is all about minimally processed foods – that means that eating whole food is a definite must – minimally cooked and with only few ingredients: that is the ideal when it comes to Whole30 policy.

Fruits

Eating food is highly recommended and encouraged, but of course, you shouldn't be exaggerating with anything. You should eat everything in moderate amounts - and to help you with that, we will be introducing a 14 day diet plan in the end of this book. Avoid fruits that have too much sugar, especially dried fruit. Also you need to take into consideration that as fruit grow during summer and spring, you will naturally eat more fruits during the season of fruits then during winter when you should eat far less fruits. Always make sure that you are eating seasonal fruits and preferably choosing organically grown fruits.

Vegetables

Huge YES to all veggies – especially green leafy veggies that are full of calcium. Yes to tomatoes, cucumbers, bell peppers, potatoes, carrots, zucchinis, spinach, kale, broccoli, cauliflower and other fresh veggies that cross your mind. Make sure you are eating lots of vegetables.

Meats

Meat is good for you as it is a source of protein and fats you need in order to be able to function properly. You can moderately eat fish and seafood, beef, turkey, chicken and even pork (although we recommend poultry and beef over pork). Fish and seafood will also come as great for your diet program as fish is rich in fatty acids and Omega-3 which is great for blood and heart, preventing heart diseases and similar conditions.

Eggs

Eggs are great as you have proteins and healthy fats by incorporating eggs into your diet. Hard boiled, baked or mixed with veggies – you will have plenty of those during your diet.

Herbs and Spices

Herbs and spices are highly encouraged and are great to use with different foods. Herbs will enhance taste of veggies and meat and allow the food to release healthy juices while being processed – again, remember that the food you are eating during Whole30 should be minimally processed.

Natural Fats

Make sure you are also introducing your body to healthy fats, but keep the list of healthy fats food limited to the previous list. All foods must comply with Whole30 program rules. So, some of the foods you can eat in order to get a healthy source of natural fat are: avocados, eggs, coconuts and coconut oil, fatty fish like salmon and herring that are also rich in omega 3 fatty acids. Say no to cheese and yoghurt because although these products are rich in fats, they also have dairy proteins that you want to avoid when on Whole30 diet.

Benefits of Whole30 Program

No one likes to think about what to eat or what not to eat, what is allowed and what's not, over thinking whether something is good for you or not – but all restricted foods within Whole30 programs are on the DON'T list for your own good. In only one month you should already be able to notice positive changes with your health and body. As a great plus, in case you have problems with obesity, sugar craves, extra pounds, high blood pressure and increased blood sugar, you will start to feel a lot better – there won't be sudden loss of energy out of the blue or feeling fatigue with no particular reason. The food allowed within Whole30 program is specifically chosen to nourish your body and to help you get back on the track with healthy living. You will be able to feel better and balanced, also looking in accordance with how you feel. Always remember that we are in fact what we eat, so say no to junk food and foods that are simply not made for you although those same food might be super tasty and mouthwatering.To help you get a grip over your new diet style, we are presenting 84 super healthy and equally tasty meals along with a 14-day diet program that will help you get started with Whole30 program in no time.

CHAPTER 2: WHOLE30 PROGRAM BREAKFAST RECIPES

It is said that breakfast is the most important meal of the day, and we agree. Breakfast will help you start your day on the right foot – that is how you will be collecting energy for the day to come so you need a breakfast packed with vitamins, fibers and protein. Check out our Whole30 suggestions for healthy and tasty breakfast recipes.

Recipe #1: Eggs and Greens Breakfast Plate

This breakfast besides from looking pretty and colorful is also packed with flavor and healthy ingredients that will help your digestive system with working properly from the moment you get up and dig into your breakfast.

Yield: 2 servings

Prep: 10 minutes

Cook: 10 minutes

Time Taken: 20 minutes

Ingredients:

- 2 cups of kale
- 1 onion – small, green, chopped
- 1 tablespoon of mint – fresh, chopped

For making dressing

- 1/2 cup of raspberries - fresh
- 1 tablespoon of vinegar – white wine
- 3 tablespoons of oil - avocado
- 3 tablespoons of water
- 8 leaves of mint – small, fresh, chopped

For topping

- 2 eggs - boiled
- 4 pieces of bacon – cooked and crisped
- 1 avocado – small

Instructions:

1. Wash the leafy greens then place them in a bowl. In the meanwhile take a skillet and the 4 pieces of bacon and fry them a bit until lightly crisped. Bake the bacon on its own grease for a couple of minutes.

2. Take your Instant Pot and place a trivet in it. Pour one cup of water into the pot and place the eggs into the trivet. Cook for 5 minutes on High pressure then allow 5 more minutes for the pressure to release.

3. While waiting for the eggs take all the ingredients for dressing and put them in a food processor. Blend until smooth. Pour over the leafy greens and stir a bit.

4. After the eggs cool a bit, peel them and cut them in halves.

5. Top the greens with crushed bacon and boiled eggs.

Recipe #2: Creamy Blueberry Breakfast Bowl

Another breakfast bowl that will help you get your morning started with nutritious and healthy breakfast that is also delicious.

Yield: 1 serving

Prep: 5 minutes

Cook: 10 minutes

Time Taken: 15 minutes

Ingredients:

- 1 sweet potato – large
- 3 tablespoons of butter – almond (ghee)
- 2 tablespoons of milk - almond

For topping

- Coconut milk – canned, full fat
- Blueberries – frozen or fresh, you can use either option
- Cinnamon – ground

Instructions:

1. Take your instant pot and place the trivet. Peel and cut the potato in bite size cubes then place it in the trivet.

2. Cook the potato for 8 minutes with the locked lid, cooking on High pressure. Use quick release then take the potatoes out and let them cool a bit.

3. Once you cooked the potato, take all the ingredients except for those under "For topping" and place them in the food processor. Blend until smooth. Place it in bowl and top it with blueberries, some cinnamon and some coconut milk. Enjoy!

Recipe #3: Apple Bowl

For all of those who love cereal for breakfast, but can't have it as cereals are big NO in Whole 30, will be thrilled with this breakfast recipe.

Yield: 1 serving

Prep: 5 minutes

Cook: 5 minutes

Time Taken: 10 minutes

Ingredients:

- ¼ cup of flour - almond
- 3 tablespoons of flax meal – golden milled
- 1 tablespoon of chia seeds - white
- 1/2 teaspoon of cinnamon - ground
- 1/8 teaspoon of salt
- 1 cup of milk - coconut
- ½ teaspoon of vanilla extract

For topping

- 3 tablespoons of apple bits - dry
- 1 apple – sliced, thinly
- Coconut milk – full fat, canned

Instructions:

1. Take your Instant Pot and place vanilla extract, 1 cup of coconut milk, cinnamon, flex meal, chia seeds and almond flour. Mix it up and seal the lid. Cook on high pressure for 2 minutes.

2. Let the pressure release naturally then open the lid and pour the cooked mixture in a serving bowl.

3. Top it with apples, dried apple bits and coconut milk. Enjoy!

Recipe #4: Whole30 Egg Toasts

When on Whole30 program you are not allowed to eat bread, so you can't have eggs and toast for breakfast. But, we have a solution that is way healthier and equally tasty.

Yield: 4 servings

Prep: 5 minutes

Cook: 10 minutes

Time Taken: 15 minutes

Ingredients:

- 2 mushrooms - portabello
- 2 tomatoes - medium
- 4 eggs
- Fresh thyme – for topping
- Salt
- Pepper
- Oil – coconut or olive
- 6 garlic cloves

Instructions:

1. Take your instant pot and add some coconut oil. Cut mushrooms and tomatoes – tomatoes should be diced and mushrooms should be halved. Add garlic on top then break the eggs on top as well.

2. Seal the lid of your instant pot then set on high pressure and cook for 10 minutes.

3. Use quick release and once the pot is medium cool, remove the lid and serve. Cut in a way that every part with the egg on top serves as one toast.

4. Combine garlic with oil with salt, pepper and thyme and dress the toast. Enjoy!

Recipe #5: Whole30 Porridge

Porridge is also not allowed in Whole30 diet, but guess what? We have a tasty and healthy alternative made especially for you.

Yield: 1 serving

Prep: 5 minutes

Cook: 5 minutes

Time Taken: 10 minutes

Ingredients:

- ¾ cup of milk - almond
- 6 tablespoons of coconut - shredded
- 3 tablespoons of flour - almond
- 2 tablespoons of flax meal – golden milled
- ½ teaspoon of vanilla extract
- cinnamon - ground
- sprinkle of salt
- 1 pear – medium, sliced, thinly

Instructions:

1. Take all ingredients except for the pear and place it in your instant pot. Mix it all up well then seal the lid and set on high pressure. Set the timer for 5 minutes.

2. Once cooked, let the pressure release naturally. Remove the lid and serve.

3. Place the cooked mixture in a bowl then top with a sliced pear and enjoy!

Recipe #6: Whole30 Breakfast Casserole

This breakfast casserole is completely Whole30 and will grant you all the energy you need for the day.

Yield: 8 servings

Prep: 5 minutes

Cook: 25 minutes

Time Taken: 30 minutes

Ingredients:

- 12 bacon slices – sugar-free
- 2 sweet potatoes – large, sliced, thinly
- 2 tablespoons of avocado butter
- 3 cups of brussel sprouts - quartered
- 1 onion – large, sliced, thinly
- 12 eggs
- 1/3 cup of coconut milk
- salt
- ¼ cup of nutritional yeast
- ½ teaspoon of garlic - powdered
- Black pepper

Instructions:

1. Take your Instant Pot and set it on Sauté option. Add bacon and garlic with avocado butter and sauté until the onions are softened and bacon is slightly crisped.

2. Next you will add brussel sprouts and sauté those in Instant pot for 5 minutes or until mildly softened.

3. Remove the mixture from the pot, but leave the oil. Arrange slices of potatoes on the bottom of your Instant pot then spread the bacon mixture across it, spreading the mixture evenly. Turn off the pot.

4. Take a bowl in the meantime and whisk the eggs, adding the rest of the ingredients from the list. Pour the mixture over the potatoes, brussel sprouts, bacon and onions.

5. Seal the lid and set the Instant Pot on Manual setting, cooking on high pressure for 15 minutes.

Recipe #7: Whole30 Breakfast Potato Salad

This is an interesting version of regular potato salad, made to be completely Whole30.

Yield: 8 servings

Prep: 10 minutes

Cook: 15 minutes

Time Taken: 25 minutes

Ingredients:

- 1 kg of potatoes - chopped
- Sea salt
- 1/3 cup of parsley – fresh, chopped
- ¾ cup of onion – medium, yellow, diced
- 2 tablespoons of lemon juice – freshly squeezed
- 2 tablespoons of mustard – sugar free
- 6 bacon slices – diced, cooked
- 4 eggs – boiled, diced
- Black pepper

Instructions:

1. Take your instant bowl and place the trivet. Pour one glass of water and turn your pot on Manual setting, cooking on high pressure. Add the eggs in the trivet and seal the lid. Cook for 5 minutes.

2. Allow the pressure to release naturally, which would take 5 more minutes. Remove the eggs.

3. Add another cup of water into the Instant pot then place the chopped potatoes in the trivet. Cook on Manual setting, cooking on high pressure for 8 minutes.

4. Use quick release and let the pot cool for a while then remove the lid and take the potatoes out. Cool them in the fridge.

5. Remove the water from the pot then add the bacon and crisp it on its own grease in the Instant pot, cooking on Sauté option.

6. Place potatoes in a bowl and add onion, parsley, mustard and lemon juice.

7. Top it with diced eggs and bacon.

Recipe #8: Whole30 Breakfast Stir Fry

This delicious breakfast bake will keep your hunger on the leash right up until your lunch time, so give it a try and you'll surely like it!

Yield: 4 servings

Prep: 10 minutes

Cook: 20 minutes

Time Taken: 30 minutes

Ingredients:

- 1 sweet potato – large, diced
- Olive oil
- 6 slices of bacon – sugar free
- 300 g of beef - ground
- 1 onion – small, chopped
- ½ cup of mushrooms – button or porcini
- 2 cups of baby spinach - fresh
- 4 eggs
- Salt
- pepper
- Scallions for garnish – fresh, chopped

Instructions:

1. Take your Instant pot and turn it on Sauté option then add some olive oil along with bacon and onion. Sauté until the onion is softened and bacon is crisped.

2. Add the ground beef and sauté while breaking it with a spoon. Cook until the beef is browned.

3. Next you will add mushrooms still cooking on sauté. Cook for about 5 minutes or until the mushrooms are softened.

4. Whisk the eggs in the meantime and add chopped spinach, salt and pepper.

5. Add potatoes to the instant pot then pour the egg mixture over it.

6. Set the pot on Manual setting and lock the lid. Cook for 15 minutes on high pressure.

7. Use quick release and serve.

8. Top with chopped scallions.

Recipe #9: Protein Breakfast Salad

This protein packed salad is everything you need to start your day – meat, fresh veggies and eggs: it doesn't get any better than that!

Yield: 4 servings

Prep: 5 minutes

Cook: 10 minutes

Time Taken: 15 minutes

Ingredients:

- 500 g of pork sausage
- 9 eggs - boiled
- 3 cups of cherry tomatoes – cut in halves
- ¼ cup of onion – purple, chopped
- 2 avocados - diced
- ½ cup of parsley - chopped
- salt
- black pepper
- 2 lemons – only juice, freshly squeezed

Instructions:

1. If you don't have pre-cooked boiled eggs, you can boil them by setting your Instant pot on Manual setting. Add a cup of water to the pot then place the trivet. Place the eggs on the trivet, seal the lid and cook for 5 minutes.

2. Allow pressure to release naturally then drain the water and remove the eggs.

3. Clean the pot then add oil. Turn sauté option on and in the meantime use the sausage meat to make meatballs.

4. Sauté the meatballs until browned, which would take about 5 minutes.

5. Mix all ingredients together in a bowl and enjoy!

Recipe #10: Fruity Coconut Breakfast Bowl

This amazing combination will make a great breakfast: it's tasty, healthy and super delicious. Of course, it's made to be all Whole30!

Yield: 1 serving

Prep: 5 minutes

Cook: 5 minutes

Time Taken: 10 minutes

Ingredients:

- 1 banana – ripe, medium
- 2 eggs
- 1 teaspoon of vanilla bean - powdered
- ¼ of apple – green, sliced, thinly
- 2 tablespoons of almond butter
- 2 tablespoons of coconut flakes - dry
- 1 teaspoon of cinnamon - ground
- Coconut oil

Instructions:

1.   First you need to create a lumpy mixture out of banana. First mash the banana with using a fork then add vanilla bean and eggs.

2.   Take the mixture and place it in your Instant pot. Seal the lid and set Manual cooking, cooking on high pressure with the timer set on 5 minutes.

3.   Once cooked, use quick release then remove the lid once it's safe.

4.   Add the mixture to a bowl and top it with apple, cinnamon, coconut flakes and almond butter.

Recipe #11: Spinach and Brussel Sprout Eggs

This recipe title basically says it all: you are in for an egg delight dish complimented with some leafy greens.

Yield: 4 servings

Prep: 5 minutes

Cook: 20 minutes

Time Taken: 25 minutes

Ingredients:

- 300 g of brussel sprouts – halved or quartered
- 300 g of baby spinach – chopped
- 1 onion – large, chopped, yellow
- 5 garlic cloves – minced
- Olive oil
- Salt
- Pepper
- 4 eggs

Instructions:

1. Turn your pot on sauté option then add some oil and onions to the pot. Sauté the onions until softened then add garlic cloves and brussel sprouts. Sauté brussel sprouts for about 5 minutes.

2. Add spinach to the instant pot then break the eggs on top and sprinkle some salt and pepper over it.

3. Lock the lid and set on Manual setting, cooking on high pressure for 10 minutes.

4. Use quick release then remove the lid once it's safe.

5. Serve and enjoy!

Recipe #12: No Grain Oatmeal

Another tasty version of Whole30 oatmeal with no grains and made to support your Whole30 program

Yield: 1 serving

Prep: 5 minutes

Cook: 5 minutes

Time Taken: 10 minutes

Ingredients:

- 1 apple – small, diced
- ¼ cup of cranberries - dry
- 1 tablespoon of chia seeds
- 1 tablespoon of coconut - unsweetened
- 1 tablespoon of almonds
- almond butter – for topping
- 1 cup of silk cashew milk

Instructions:

1. Take the apple and dice it to small pieces then take the apple bits and all other ingredients except for almond butter and cashew milk and place them in a food processor. Blend until grainy.

2. Place the grainy mixture in the Instant Pot with cashew milk and seal the lid.

3. Set on Manual setting, cooking on high pressure for 2 minutes.

4. Let the pressure release naturally then serve and top with coconut cream or eat as it is.

5. Enjoy!

Recipe #13: Egg and Kale Quiche

This breakfast thrill with potato crust will set you up for a busy morning in no time!

Yield: 8 servings

Prep: 10 minutes

Cook: 30 minutes

Time Taken: 40 minutes

Ingredients:

- 2 sweet potatoes - medium
- 1 sweet onion - small
- 2 cups of kale
- 1 broccoli floret - small
- 2 garlic cloves
- 2 eggs
- 2 egg whites
- 1 tablespoon of nutrition yeast
- 1 cup of coconut milk - canned
- kosher salt
- black pepper

Instructions:

1. Set your Instant pot on sauté option and add some oil and onions with garlic.
2. Sauté until the garlic and onions are softened and translucent.
3. Next you will add the potatoes and broccoli and sauté for 5 minutes more.
4. Add kale as well, then take a bowl and whisk the eggs with coconut milk, salt, pepper, nutrition yeast and eggs and egg whites.
5. Clean the pot then insert a casserole dish and pour the veggie mixture in it.
6. Pour the egg mixture over the ingredients in the Instant pot then seal the lid.
7. Cook for 30 minutes on high pressure, Manual setting.
8. Allow the pressure to release naturally.
9. Serve and enjoy!

Recipe #14: Eggs Benedict with Asparagus

This Eggs Benedict recipe is completely Whole30 friendly and thus we won't be serving English muffins. Instead we will show you how to prepare asparagus instead of muffins we don't need.

Yield: 4 servings

Prep: 5 minutes

Cook: 10 minutes

Time Taken: 15 minutes

Ingredients:

- 8 stalks of asparagus - large
- 4 eggs - large
- 2 teaspoons of vinegar – apple cider
- Chives – for garnish

Hollandaise Sauce Ingredients

- 2 egg yolks - large
- ¼ cup of avocado butter - melted
- 2 teaspoons of lemon juice – freshly squeezed
- ¼ teaspoon of paprika
- Salt

Instructions:

1. Each egg should be broken in a single ramekin.
2. Thinly slice the asparagus and trim it then take your Instant pot and set it on Sauté option.
3. Add a cup of water and add the asparagus once the water starts boiling. Cook the asparagus for 5 minutes then lower the temperature and add vinegar to the water.
4. Then you will slide all eggs into the water and shape them with molds – you can also allow them to cook without molds.
5. Seal the lid and cook on High pressure, Manual setting for 5 minutes.
6. In the meantime you will make a sauce.
7. Put all the ingredients except for the butter into the food processor and blend it all together. Lower the speed then slowly add the butter as you are blending. Allow the sauce to thicken then switch off the food processor.
8. Quick release the pressure, then take out the eggs and asparagus.
9. Dry the eggs on paper towels then serve with sauce and chives on top.

Recipe #15: Korean Eggs

Eggs come as inevitable part of healthy diet in the morning, so we thought of making eggs fun again by presenting a Korean version of steamed eggs.

Yield: 1 serving

Prep: 5 minutes

Cook: 5 minutes

Time Taken: 10 minutes

Ingredients:

- 1 egg
- 1/3 cup of water - cold
- 1 teaspoon of scallions - chopped
- Sesame seeds - pinch
- Garlic salt – powdered, pinch
- Pepper – pinch

Instructions:

1.   First you will mix the egg with water and then pour it over a strainer with a bowl placed beneath. Press the mixture to the strainer then combine the rest of the ingredients with the eggs in the bowl.

2.   Place the mixture on the trivet and pour one cup of water to the bottom of the pot.

3.   Seal the lid and set on Manual, cooking on high pressure for 5 minutes.

4.   Quick release the pressure then serve and enjoy!

5.   You can serve Korean eggs with cauliflower rice.

Recipe #16: Instant Pot Muffins

Muffins for breakfast are less likely to happen on Whole30 diet, but that is not the case with these Instant Pot Muffins as all ingredients are Whole30 compliant.

Yield: 1 serving

Prep: 5 minutes

Cook: 8 minutes

Time Taken: 13 minutes

Ingredients:

4 eggs

¼ teaspoon of lemon pepper seasoning

4 slices of bacon – crumbled

1 green onion - diced

- ½ cup of almond flour

Instructions:

1. Whisk the eggs and add lemon pepper seasoning and almond flour.

2. Pour the mixture into muffin cups and sprinkle with scallions and crumbled bacon.

3. Pour one cup of water into the pot and place the trivet. Place the muffin cups on the trivet.

4. Seal the lid and set on Manual cooking, cooking on high pressure for 8 minutes.

5. Quick release the pressure and serve!

Recipe #17: Apple and Squash Porridge

This creamy Whole30 porridge will surely make your morning brighter!

Yield: 3 servings

Prep: 5 minutes

Cook: 8 minutes

Time Taken: 13 minutes

Ingredients:

- 2 apples – large, peeled, cored, sliced
- 1 delicata squash – whole, uncut
- ½ cup of water
- 2 tablespoons of gelatin
- 1/2 teaspoon of cinnamon
- 1/8 teaspoon of cloves
- 1/8 teaspoon of ginger - mashed
- pinch of sea salt

Instructions:

1. Place the squash with apple slices and water with spices into the pot.

2. Seal the lid and set on Manual, cooking on high pressure for 8 minutes.

3. Allow the pressure to release naturally and then remove the squash and the rest of the contents.

4. Cut the squash in half and then deseed it and scrape the meat out. Place the squash and apples with spices into a food processor and blend until smooth.

5. Add gelatin and salt in the end and then pulse again until smoothened out.

6. Serve and enjoy!

Recipe #18: Meat Quiche

This recipe is for anyone looking for a breakfast that will keep you going a long way till noon.

Yield: 4 servings

Prep: 5 minutes

Cook: 30 minutes

Time Taken: 35 minutes

Ingredients:

- 6 eggs
- ½ cup of almond milk
- ¼ teaspoon of salt
- 1/8 teaspoon of black pepper - ground
- 4 slices of bacon – crumbled, cooked
- 1 cup of ground sausage
- ½ cup of ham - diced
- 2 green onions – chopped
- 1 tablespoon of almond flour

Instructions:

1. Place ham, sausage, onions and bacon in a casserole dish that can fit into your Instant Pot.

2. Then, whisk the eggs with milk, salt, pepper and almond flour.

3. Pour the egg mixture over the meat and onions.

4. Place the dish on the trivet and pour one cup of water into the pot.

5. Seal the lid and set on Manual cooking, cooking on high pressure for 30 minutes.

6. When the cooking is done wait for 10 minutes then use the quick release for releasing the pressure.

7. Serve and enjoy!

Recipe #19: Whole30 Burrito

No burritos allowed except when we are making it this way! Check this recipe out – you will surely have it more than once.

Yield: 1 serving

Prep: 5 minutes

Cook: 10 minutes

Time Taken: 15 minutes

Ingredients:

- 4 slices of ham – pre cooked
- 2 eggs
- ¼ cup of mixed, chopped veggies – baby spinach, black olives, tomato and bell pepper
- Salsa or guacamole

Instructions:

1. Set your Instant pot on sauté option then add the veggie mixture with some oil. Sauté until mildly softened which would take about 2 minutes.

2. Next whisk the eggs and add them to the veggies, mixing it all up and stirring while still on Sauté option.

3. Switch from Sauté to Manual setting then seal the lid and cook on high pressure for 5 minutes.

4. Allow the pressure to release naturally.

5. Use the veggie-egg cooked mixture to fill ham slices.

6. Clean Instant pot and add some more oil, switching back to Sauté option.

7. Sauté the slices with filling for a minute or two.

8. Top it with salsa or guacamole and enjoy.

Recipe #20: Potato and Zucchini Bake

This tasty faux bake is made of potato and zucchinis with your Instant Pot for a quick and nutritious breakfast.

Yield: 4 servings

Prep: 5 minutes

Cook: 20 minutes

Time Taken: 25 minutes

Ingredients:

- 1 cup zucchini - shredded
- 1 cup of sweet potato - shredded
- 1 egg - whisked
- 1 tablespoon of coconut flour
- ½ cup of coconut milk
- ½ teaspoon of garlic - powdered
- ¼ teaspoon of cumin - ground
- ½ teaspoon of parsley - dry
- Salt
- Pepper
- 1 tablespoon of avocado butter
- 1 tablespoon of oil – olive, extra virgin

Instructions:

1. Mix the zucchinis and potatoes together in one bowl with whisked egg then mix coconut flour and other spices and dry ingredients in other bowl.

2. Combine the two mixtures together.

3. Place in an insert dish that is previously greased up with avocado butter then pour one cup of water in the Instant pot.

4. Seal the lid and set on Manual setting, cooking on high pressure for 20 minutes.

5. Allow pressure to release naturally then cut and serve!

Recipe #21: Poached Eggs

Another great recipe idea for making your breakfast eggs with Instant Pot!

Yield: 2 servings

Prep: 10 minutes

Cook: 1o minutes

Time Taken: 20 minutes

Ingredients:

- 2 eggs
- 1 tablespoon of bacon – cooked, chopped
- 2 tablespoons of avocado butter
- 1 jalapeno pepper - sliced
- ½ cup of onion - diced
- 1 tablespoon of cilantro - chopped
- 1 teaspoon of Taco seasoning

Instructions:

1. Turn your pot on Sauté and add bacon an avocado butter. Sauté until the bacon is slightly crisped then add onions, jalapeno, cilantro and taco seasoning, stirring in to mix all up well.

2. Sauté for a couple of minutes, then break the eggs over the mixture.

3. Seal the lid and set on high pressure, Manual cooking. Cook for 1 minute then use quick release.

4. Serve and enjoy!

CHAPTER 3: WHOLE30 PROGRAM LUNCH RECIPES

When it is time for lunch, one is for sure – you won't be running to a fast food restaurant as junk food is strictly prohibited during Whole30 program. Instead, you will be having healthy and delicious meals that are made especially to comply with Whole30 menu.

Recipe #22: Beef and Potato Bake

This is a classic dish made to be completely Whole30 and nothing less tasty than the original version of the recipe.

Yield: 4 servings
Prep: 5 minutes
Cook: 20 minutes
Time Taken: 25 minutes

Ingredients:

- 500 g beef – ground
- 1 onion – large, yellow, diced
- Cup of mushrooms – sliced
- 2 tomatoes – peeled, ripe, diced
- 5 garlic cloves
- 2 sweet potatoes – large
- Salt
- Pepper
- Olive oil

Instructions:

1. First take your Instant pot and turn it on Sauté option. Add oil then heat it up and add the onions. Cook the onions until soft and browned.
2. Next add the garlic then the meat. Sauté until the meat is browned, then add salt, pepper and garlic and stir in.
3. Add the tomatoes and cook until there is very little juices remained in pot.
4. Add the mushrooms and cook until the mushrooms are softened and slightly browned.
5. Arrange sliced potatoes into the insert dish. Clean the pot and remove the mixture.
6. Add the trivet then place the dish on it. Pour one cup of water into the Instant pot then arrange the mixture with meat on top of potatoes.
7. Seal the lid and set the pot on Manual setting, cooking on High pressure for 20 minutes.
8. Quick release, then serve and enjoy!

Recipe #23: Turkey Burgers

Everyone loves burgers, but since you are not allowed to eat fast food and junk food, we have come up with an amazing substitute with turkey meat as a main star of the dish.

Yield: 4 servings

Prep: 10 minutes

Cook: 10 minutes

Time Taken: 20 minutes

Ingredients:

- 500 g turkey - ground
- 1 jalapeño pepper – seeded, thinly sliced
- 1 medium shallot – medium, peeled, sliced
- 1 lime – zest and juice
- 2 tablespoons of cilantro
- 1 teaspoon of paprika
- 1 teaspoon of cumin
- sea salt
- black pepper

Instructions:

1. Combine turkey meat with lime, spices and herbs along with salt and pepper and lime zest.

2. Combine well and make patties out of the meat.

3. Take your Instant pot and turn on Sauté option. Add the oil then add patties and cook until the patties are browned on all sides.

4. In case your meat is to wet when making the meat mixture, dry the patties on paper towel before cooking.

5. Serve with guacamole, salsa, salads or baked potatoes instead of French fries.

Recipe #24: Poached Salmon

Cold poached salmon is a true delight in the world of Whole30 program as it is a perfect source of good taste and fatty omega 3 acids.

Yield: 4 servings

Prep: 5 minutes

Cook: 25 minutes

Time Taken: 30 minutes

Ingredients:

- 1 salmon – fillet, large
- 2 tablespoons of oil - olive
- 1 onion – medium, chopped
- 3 garlic cloves - minced
- ¼ cup of parsley – fresh, chopped
- 1 tablespoon of thyme – fresh, chopped
- 1 lemon – sliced
- 1 lemon - juiced
- Water to cover the salmon
- salt
- pepper

Instructions:

1. Take Instant pot and turn it on Sauté option then add olive oil, once heated add the onions and garlic. Sauté until softened.

2. Add all the herbs and spices along with the lemon juice and sliced lemon then cook some more. Then add the water, about 4 cups and bring the mixture to simmer. Cook for about 10 minutes until water is infused with flavors.

3. Place salmon in the water and set the Pot on high pressure, Manual setting and cook for 5 minutes.

4. Allow the pressure to release naturally then remove the lid and take the salmon out of the water.

5. Cool before serving and serve with salad like cucumbers or tomatoes.

Recipe #25: Kale and Sausage Sauté

This easy and simple to make lunch will surely thrill you as you will feel full until dinner time, having been eaten this simple but amazing protein packed dish.

Yield: 4 servings

Prep: 5 minutes

Cook: 15 minutes

Time Taken: 20 minutes

Ingredients:

- 500 g sausage
- 1 bunch of kale – leaves only
- 1 onion – medium, diced
- 1 bell pepper – red, chopped

Instructions:

1. Remove the sausage from its casing and add it to the Instant pot with some olive oil. Instant pot should be switched to Sauté option.

2. Brown the sausage then add the onions.

3. Cook everything together until the onions are softened. Add the red bell pepper and cook for a couple of more minutes

4. Add kale at the end and sauté for a couple of more minutes.

5. Serve and enjoy!

Recipe #26: Pesto Chicken

Poultry, chicken particularly, is light meat that will grant you the proteins and fibers you need without having you bloated or feeling discomfort after you have had your lunch. Try this excellent version of baked chicken with pesto sauce.

Yield: 4 servings

Prep: 5 minutes

Cook: 10 minutes

Time Taken: 15 minutes

Ingredients:

For pesto

- 3 cups of basil – fresh, leaves only
- 2 cups of baby spinach – fresh, leaves only
- 4 garlic cloves
- 2/3 cups of oil - olive
- salt
- 2 tablespoons of nutritional yeast

For Chicken

- 700 g of chicken breasts – no skin, boneless
- sea salt
- pepper
- 4 slices of tomato
- Italian seasoning

Instructions:

1. First make pesto by putting all ingredients listed under pesto, into a food processor. Blend until smooth then store in a sealed jar – you can keep it in the fridge.

2. Take your Instant pot and turn it on Poultry setting. Add some oil then add the chicken breasts and 1 cup of water with Italian seasoning, salt and pepper. Seal the lid and cook for 6 minutes on high pressure.

3. Allow the pressure to release naturally.

4. Take the chicken out and drain the water.

5. Clean the pot then switch it to Sauté option. Add some oil then sauté tomato slices for a couple of minutes.

6. Spread pesto on the chicken then sauté the chicken with sautéed tomatoes placed on the top.

7. Remove the chicken after 5 minutes and serve!

Recipe #27: Rosemary Chicken with Lemon

Another great Whole30 friendly recipe with chicken as a main star. This time, the poultry is complimented with lemon and rosemary.

Yield: 4 servings

Prep: 5 minutes

Cook: 15 minutes

Time Taken: 20 minutes

Ingredients:

- ¼ cup of oil - olive
- 4 pieces of chicken breasts – no skin, boneless
- 1 sweet potato – cut in cubes
- 1 lemon – large, juiced
- 1 lemon – large, sliced
- 2 tablespoons of rosemary
- 5 garlic cloves - mashed
- Salt
- Pepper

Instructions:

1.   Take instant pot and turn it on Stew option. Place all ingredients together in the pot, first adding the oil, chicken breasts and potatoes, then adding the rest of the ingredients.

2.   Seal the lid and cook on Stew option on high pressure for 15 minutes.

3.   Allow pressure to release naturally then open the lid and serve!

Recipe #28: Lime and Chili Salmon

Another great recipe with salmon as the main ingredient, complimented with bold and daring combination of hot and sour flavors.

Yield: 4 servings

Prep: 5 minutes

Cook: 10 minutes

Time Taken: 15 minutes

Ingredients:

- 2 limes - juiced
- ¼ cup of parsley – fresh, chopped
- 2 tablespoons of oil - olive
- 2 tablespoons of water
- 4 garlic cloves - mashed
- 1 tablespoon of red chili - flakes
- 1 teaspoon of cumin - ground
- salt
- 4 salmon fillets
- 1 bell pepper – red, chopped
- 1 bell pepper – green, chopped
- 1 bell pepper – yellow, chopped
- 1 onion – medium, cut in wedges, yellow

Instructions:

1.   Take the insert dish for your Instant Pot and turn it on Manual setting. Arrange the fillets in the greased up dish than add the dish to the pot.

2.   Pour one cup of water at the bottom of the Instant pot.

3.   Take all ingredients except for bell peppers and onion and whisk them all together. Then, mix the liquid you have made with onions and peppers and pour it over the salmon filets, spreading it evenly across the dish.

4.   Seal the lid and cook on Manual setting, cooking on high pressure for 10 minutes.

5.   Quick release then serve and enjoy!

Recipe #29: Tomato Soup

We mostly eat hard food, but our stomachs really feel good when introduced to a warm delight like soups - that is why we are suggesting this tomato soup for lunch – starring roasted tomatoes.

Yield: 6 servings

Prep: 5 minutes

Cook: 45 minutes

Time Taken: 50 minutes

Ingredients:

- 2 cans of tomatoes – peeled
- 6 garlic cloves – mashed
- 8 sprigs of thyme – fresh
- 2 tablespoons of oil – olive
- Kosher salt
- black pepper
- Red pepper flakes
- 1 onion – yellow, large, diced
- ¼ cup of tomato paste
- 4 cups of vegetable broth – low-sodium

Instructions:

1. First you will take care of roasting by preheating the oven and taking a baking pan and placing a baking sheet on it. Place halved tomatoes on the sheet then sprinkle with garlic, thyme, salt, pepper, red pepper flakes and olive oil – spread evenly. Roast for 30 to 35 minutes.

2. Take your Instant pot then add some oil and onions. Cook on Sauté option until the onions are softened.

3. Next add the leftover tomatoes from the cans and add vegetable broth to the pot.

4. Remove thyme sprigs from roasted tomatoes and transfer everything from the baking pan into the Instant pot.

5. Seal the lid and cook on Soup option for 10 minutes on high pressure.

Recipe #30: Coconut Chicken Soup

This exotic soup will surely warm you up and give you everything you are looking for in a lunch – it's light but nutritious so give it a try and you won't regret it.

Yield: 4 servings

Prep: 5 minutes

Cook: 15 minutes

Time Taken: 20 minutes

Ingredients:

- 1 can of chicken stock
- ½ cup of coconut cream
- 1 tablespoon of fish sauce
- 2 teaspoons of ginger – mashed, fresh
- 2 teaspoons of lemongrass paste
- 2 carrots – medium, diced
- 2 parsnips – medium, diced
- 1 potato – diced, medium
- 500 g of chicken breasts - no skin, boneless
- 1 onion – small, red, diced
- 6 cilantro sprigs
- 1 lime – large, juiced

Instructions:

1.   Pour coconut cream, ginger, fish sauce, lemongrass paste and chicken stock in your Instant pot and turn Sauté option. Bring the mixture to simmer.

2.   Then, you will add carrots, parsnips, potatoes and chicken cubes to the pot and seal the lid, changing the option to Manual, cooking on high pressure for 15 minutes.

3.   Once cooked, allow the pressure to release naturally and let the pot cool a bit before removing the lid.

4.   Add cilantro, onion and lime juice before serving.

5.   Enjoy!

Recipe #31: Prosciutto Pork Wrap

We have already had mangos wrapped in prosciutto for breakfast, and now let's try this marvelously tasteful prosciutto pork wrap.

Yield: 6 servings

Prep: 5 minutes

Cook: 15 minutes

Time Taken: 20 minutes

Ingredients:

- 11 kg of pork tenderloin
- 6 slices of prosciutto – large, thin
- ¼ cup of mustard – sugar-free
- salt
- pepper

Instructions:

1.   Take your instant pot and add the insert dish. Grease up the dish and pour one cup of water in the Instant pot.

2.   Take prosciutto slices and arrange them one by one on the bottom of the insert dish. Spread mustard over the slices, covering all parts and edges.

3.   Place the pork tenderloin onto the edge of arranged slices and wrap it up.

4.   Sprinkle with salt and pepper then seal the lid and turn on Meat setting and cook on high pressure for 15 minutes.

5.   Allow the pressure to release naturally and wait for the pot to cool before removing the lid.

6.   Serve sliced and enjoy!

Recipe #32: Sausage and Chicken One Pan Dish

Everything you need in a lunch is placed in this one pan dish that is easy and simple to make, but healthy and delicious.

Yield: 8 servings

Prep: 5 minutes

Cook: 10 minutes

Time Taken: 15 minutes

Ingredients:

- 8 pieces of chicken – with bones
- 500 g of potatoes – red or baby red, halved or quartered
- 6 pieces of sausage - precooked
- 1 onion – red, large, quartered
- 1 lemon - juiced
- ¼ cup of oil - olive
- 4 garlic cloves - chopped
- 1 tablespoon of paprika - smoked
- Chili flakes – just a pinch
- salt
- pepper

Instructions:

1. Take the chicken, sausage cut in big chunks, potatoes and onions and arrange them across the greased up Instant pot.

2. Combine the rest of the ingredients into a bowl and whisk it all together. Pour the marinade over the chicken and veggies and seal the lid.

3. Set on Manual setting and cook on high pressure for 10 minutes.

4. Allow the pressure to release naturally then open the lid and serve.

Recipe #33: Mushrooms and Coconut Chicken

This dish is using a well known combination of white chicken meat, mushrooms and coconut cream. It is pretty easy to be made and even easier to wipe out of your plate.

Yield: 4 servings

Prep: 10 minutes

Cook: 10 minutes

Time Taken: 20 minutes

Ingredients:

- 1 kg of chicken breasts – boneless, no skin
- 500 g of mushrooms – porcini or button
- 6 garlic cloves – diced
- 1 onion – large, yellow, diced
- 1 teaspoon oregano
- Salt
- Pepper
- 1 cup of coconut cream

Instructions:

1. Take your instant pot and add some oil, adding onions and garlic to the pot. Set on Sauté option and cook until softened.

2. Add the chicken breasts to onions and garlic and brown them on all sides.

3. Next you will add salt, pepper, coconut cream, oregano and mushrooms.

4. Seal the lid and set on Manual option. Cook on high pressure for 10 minutes.

5. Allow the pressure to release naturally, let it cool then serve and enjoy!

Recipe #34: Italian Chicken

Travel to Italy while following the taste of this easy to make and delicious chicken, inspired by Italian cuisine.

Yield: 4 servings

Prep: 10 minutes

Cook: 10 minutes

Time Taken: 20 minutes

Ingredients:

- 4 pieces of chicken breasts – boneless, no skin
- 1 tablespoon of oil - olive
- 1 onion – large, chopped
- 3 garlic cloves - chopped
- 1 can of tomatoes - crushed
- 1 cup of cherry tomatoes
- ½ cup of olives - pitted
- ¼ cup of basil – fresh, chopped, for garnish
- Salt
- Pepper

Instructions:

1. Turn your Instant pot on Sauté option and add some oil. Add the chicken and brown it on all sides.
2. Remove the chicken then add onions and garlic and sauté until softened.
3. Get the chicken back to the pot then add tomatoes, salt and pepper.
4. Seal the lid and set to Poultry option, cooking on high pressure with timer set on 10 minutes.
5. Allow the pressure to release naturally then remove the lid and serve.
6. Garnish with basil and enjoy!

Recipe #35: Greek One Pan Lunch

Another one pan lunch dish, now made to be prepared all in one pan with amazing set of different tastes that will take you to a trip to Greece.

Yield: 4 servings

Prep: 5 minutes

Cook: 15 minutes

Time Taken: 20 minutes

Ingredients:

For marinade

- 3 tablespoons of oil - olive
- 2 tablespoons of lemon juice – freshly squeezed
- 4 garlic cloves - mashed
- salt
- pepper
- 2 teaspoons of paprika
- 2 teaspoons of oregano - dry

For Chicken and Vegetables

- 4 pieces of chicken breasts – boneless, no skin
- 2 red peppers – seeded, thinly sliced
- 1 onion – large, red, cut into wedges
- 8 garlic cloves - whole
- 500 g of baby potatoes - halved
- ¼ cup of olives - pitted
- 2 lemons – halved

Instructions:

1. Turn your Instant pot on Manual setting and sprinkle it with oil then start arranging all veggies, meat and lemons across the pot.

2. Take all ingredients for marinade then whisk them in a bowl. Pour the marinade evenly over the veggies and meat.

3. Seal the lid and cook on Manual on high pressure for 15 minutes.

4. Allow the pressure to release naturally then remove the lid once the pot is cool.

5. Garnish with olives and enjoy!

Recipe #36: Brussel Sprout Apple and Bacon Roast

For light and nutritious lunch that you can even take to work as a take out, this recipe is surely going to tickle your senses and nurture you till dinner time.

Yield: 4 servings

Prep: 10 minutes

Cook: 5 minutes

Time Taken: 15 minutes

Ingredients:

- 500 g of brussel sprouts - halved
- 2 teaspoon of oil – olive
- salt
- 1 apple – sweet crisp, medium
- 4 slices of bacon – sugar free
- 1 tablespoon of rosemary – fresh, chopped
- Pepper

Instructions:

1. Preheat the oven and place brussel sprouts on the baking pan, over the baking sheet. Sprinkle with some salt and olive oil then place in the oven and roast for 10 minutes.

2. Next you will take your instant pot and set it on Sauté option. Add the oil then add 1 diced apple and bacon. Sauté until apples and bacon are crisped.

3. Add brussel sprouts and add them to the pot and add pepper. Seal the lid and set on Manual, cooking on high pressure for 5 minutes.

4. Allow the pressure to release naturally then remove the lid.

5. Serve and enjoy!

Recipe #37: Whole30 Sloppy Joe's

Kids love Sloppy Joe's and even barely any grown up is able to resist these because it gets you back right your childhood. Look how you can make Whole3o Sloppy Joe's for a family lunch.

Yield: 4 servings

Prep: 10 minutes

Cook: 15 minutes

Time Taken: 25 minutes

Ingredients:

- 4 sweet potatoes – medium or large, one per person
- 1 teaspoon of coconut oil – for baking
- Salt – for baking

Sauce

- 3 medjool dates – pitted and cut
- ¼ cup of water – for soaking
- ¼ cup of tomato paste
- 1 cup of tomato sauce – without salt
- 3 ½ tablespoons of vinegar – apple cider
- 1 tablespoon of coconut aminos
- 1 teaspoon of brown mustard – sugar free
- 1 teaspoon of onion - powdered
- 1 teaspoon of garlic - powdered
- 1 teaspoon of smoked paprika
- salt

For the beef

- 500 g of beef – lean, ground
- Olive oil
- ½ bell pepper – green, diced
- ½ bell pepper – red, diced
- 1 onion – small, yellow, chopped
- 1 garlic clove - mashed
- salt

Instructions:

1.   Take a food processor and put water, dates and tomato paste in it. Blend until smooth then add the rest of the ingredients for sauce and bled until completely smooth and combined.

2.   Turn on your Instant pot then switch it to Sauté option and add some oil, add the ground beef then brown it a bit before adding the onions. Cook until the onions are softened and browned.

3.   Next add the peppers and garlic then cook some more while stirring in. Cook until the peppers are softer, for about 2 minutes.

4.   Next take the potatoes and cut them in half. Remove some of the insides but leave some "meat". Fill with the beef toping you have made.

5.   Clean the pot then take the insert dish and grease it up. Add the trivet and place the dish on top also pouring one cup of water to the pot. Arrange the filled potatoes across the dish then seal the lid and set on Manual, cooking on high pressure for 15 minutes.

6.   Allow the pressure to release naturally then open the lid and serve!

Recipe #38: Taco Soup

Taco is among top several foods originated in Mexican cuisine so no wonder this word provokes mouthwatering reaction. Try this amazing Taco Soup, inspired by popular Mexican cuisine.

Yield: 6 servings

Prep: 10 minutes

Cook: 10 minutes

Time Taken: 20 minutes

Ingredients:

- 2 tablespoons of avocado butter
- 1 onion – large, diced
- 4 bell peppers – colorful, diced
- 1 kg of beef - lean, ground
- 2 teaspoons of chili - powdered
- 2 tablespoons of cumin
- salt
- pepper
- 1 teaspoon of paprika
- 1 teaspoon of cinnamon
- 1 teaspoon of garlic - powdered
- 1 teaspoon of onion - powdered
- ¼ teaspoon of cayenne pepper
- 2 cans of tomatoes – diced
- 2 cans of broth – beef
- ½ cup of coconut milk
- ½ cup of green chiles – diced

Instructions:

1. Turn on your Instant pot to Sauté option and add the avocado butter. Once the butter is melted, take the onions and bell pepper and cook them for about 5 minutes or until soft and tender.
2. Next you will take the ground beef and add it to the pot then stir. You will be cooking beef until browned.
3. Once the beef is browned and the veggies soft, add all the spices from the list.
4. In the end take coconut milk, tomatoes, green chiles and broth and pour everything into the pot.
5. Switch to Soup/Stew option and cook for 10 minutes on high pressure.
6. Allow the pressure to release naturally.
7. Serve with lime juice, avocados or chopped green onions.

Recipe #39: Bruschetta Chicken

No bruschetta bread allowed in Whole30, but instead you can use the same ingredients you would use with bread while making this delicious chicken, made in your own Instant pot.

Yield: 4 servings

Prep: 10 minutes

Cook: 15 minutes

Time Taken: 25 minutes

Ingredients:

- 700 g of chicken breasts – boneless, no skin, sliced
- 1 cup of tomatoes – diced, fresh
- 1 tablespoon of basil – chopped, fresh, leaves only
- 1 teaspoon of oil – olive, extra virgin
- salt
- pepper
- 1 cup of vinegar – balsamic

Instructions:

1. Turn your Instant pot on sauté option and add some oil. Season the chicken with salt and pepper than sauté it on each side until ready and browned.

2. In the meanwhile, take all ingredients and mix them in a bowl, except for balsamic vinegar. Pour over the chicken.

3. Switch to Poultry option and seal the lid. Cook on high pressure for 15 minutes.

4. Allow the pressure to release naturally then switch to Sauté option.

5. Add vinegar and let it simmer with the chicken.

6. Serve and enjoy!

Recipe #40: Beef Skillet with Sweet Potatoes and Zucchinis

Half of the ingredients included are already mentioned in the title of this dish, so take a glance at the ingredient list and hit the store so you could find all items you need to prepare this beef delish.

Yield: 4 servings

Prep: 10 minutes

Cook: 10 minutes

Time Taken: 20 minutes

Ingredients:

- 1 tablespoon of oil - olive
- 500 g of beef – ground, lean
- 2 garlic cloves - mashed
- 1 onion – small, diced
- 1 bell pepper – small, red, diced
- 2 cups of sweet potatoes - diced
- ¼ cup of broth - beef
- 1 zucchini – medium, quartered
- 1 teaspoon of mustard – sugar free
- 1/3 cup of tomato sauce
- ½ teaspoon of oregano - dry
- Pinch of red pepper - crushed
- Salt
- Black pepper – freshly ground
- Parsley – fresh, chopped

Instructions:

1. Take your Instant pot and turn on Sauté option. Add some oil.
2. Add the beef and garlic and stir cook it for about 5 minutes or until browned.
3. Next you will add onions and bell pepper to the pot and sauté for 3 minutes longer.
4. Then, you will add the broth, diced potatoes and zucchinis with the rest of the ingredients except for parsley and seal the lid.
5. Cook on Manual setting for 10 minutes on high pressure.
6. Allow the pressure to release naturally then open the lid.
7. Use parsley for garnish and enjoy your lunch!

Recipe #41: Carrot Chicken Roast

Chicken roast is a must-cook classic even in the world of Whole30, so we are presenting this great recipe for making a tasty and healthy roasted chicken with veggies with your Instant pot in no time.

Yield: 8 servings

Prep: 5 minutes

Cook: 15 minutes

Time Taken: 20 minutes

Ingredients:

- 8 pieces of chicken thighs – trimmed, with skin
- 2 cups of parsnips - diced
- 2 cups of carrots - diced
- 2 cups of sweet potatoes - diced
- ¼ cup of oil - olive
- 2 tablespoons of rosemary – fresh, chopped
- ½ lemon – juiced
- ½ lemon - sliced
- Salt
- Pepper

Instructions:

1.   Switch your Instant pot on Manual setting then grease it up. 7

2.   Arrange the chicken thighs on the bottom of the pot.

3.   Take all veggies from the list and place them in a bowl then add rosemary, lemon juice, olive oil and salt and pepper. Mix it all together then evenly spread across the chicken.

4.   Top with lemon slices then seal the lid and cook on Manual setting on high pressure for 15 minutes.

5.   Quick release the valve then remove the lid.

6.   Serve and enjoy!

Recipe #42: Cajun Style Shrimp Wraps

Another one of those types of lunches you can take to work and have a healthy and fresh Whole30 meal. This time we are picking shrimps as one of the seafood's finest products, wrapped in lettuce and prepared Cajun style.

Yield: 4 servings

Prep: 5 minutes

Cook: 3 minutes

Time Taken: 8 minutes

Ingredients:

- 500 g of shrimps - large
- 1 tablespoon of lime juice
- Cajun seasoning
- 1 tablespoon of oil - olive
- Lettuce wraps

For Cajun Seasoning

- 1 teaspoon of salt
- 1 teaspoon of garlic - powdered
- 1 teaspoon of onion - powdered
- 1 teaspoon of black pepper – ground, fresh
- 1 teaspoon of oregano - dry
- 2 teaspoons of paprika
- Pinch of cayenne pepper

Instructions:

1. Take shrimps and clean them then place them in a bowl.
2. Make Cajun seasoning by combining and whisking all ingredients for Cajun seasoning listed above.
3. Add lime juice then add oil and Cajun seasoning, mixing all ingredients together.
4. Turn instant pot to Fish option and cook on high pressure with sealed lid for 3 minutes.
5. Quick release and remove the lid once the pot is cool.
6. Garnish with green onions and place in lettuce wraps then serve and enjoy!

CHAPTER 4: WHOLE30 PROGRAM DINNER RECIPES

Dinner should be nutritious, healthy and light and preferably you shouldn't eat at least 3 to 4 hours before going to sleep because your digestion system would get "confused" – eating late in the evening and sneaking up to the fridge in the late hours at night may lead to excessive pounds and obesity. That is why we are presenting light, tasty and nutritious dinner dishes.

Recipe #43: Greek Salad

Another Greek inspired dish on the line – this time we are trying out Whole30 dinner salad packed with tastes characteristic for Greece.

Yield: 1 serving

Prep: 5 minutes

Cook: 10 minutes

Time Taken: 15 minutes

Ingredients:

- 1 bunch of arugula
- salad mix – one cup
- 1 piece of chicken breasts - cubed
- ¼ cup of olives – pitted
- 1 tomato - sliced
- 1 egg – hardboiled, sliced
- Red onion slices – per taste
- Greek Dressing or other dressing compliant to Whole30
- 1 tablespoon of oil - olive

Instructions:

1. Take the chicken cubes and set in the Instant pot with one tablespoon of olive oil. Seal the lid and set on Poultry option. Cook on high pressure for 6 minutes.

2. Once the time is up, allow the pressure to release naturally then take the chicken bits out.

3. In case you haven't cooked the egg previously, clean the pot and take the trivet. Place it in the pot and pour one cup of water then place the egg on the trivet and seal the lid.

4. Set on Manual and cook for 5 minutes on high pressure.

5. Allow the pressure to release naturally.

6. Mix all ingredients in a bowl and coat with Greek dressing. Enjoy!

Recipe #44: Salmon and Veggies Salad Plate

This dinner salad is everything you are looking for in your meal – there is a tender and tasty salmon filet along with fresh veggies to compliment the fish and grant you a light and nutritious dinner.

Yield: 1 serving

Prep: 10 minutes

Cook: 5 minutes

Time Taken: 15 minutes

Ingredients:

- 100 g salmon filet
- 50 g of French greens
- 1 cup of cherry tomatoes – halved, salted
- 2 tablespoons of red onions with olive oil and oregano – you can make this in a cup with diced red onions
- ½ of cucumber - sliced
- 3 handfuls of mixed salads
- ¼ cup of olives - pitted
- Chives – chopped, for garnish

For making dressing

- ¼ cup of fresh lemon juice
- ½ cup of olive oil
- 1 garlic clove - mashed
- salt
- pepper
- 2 tablespoon of chives

Instructions:

1.   Turn your instant pot to Manual option and add some oil, French greens and the salmon. Add a cup of water and seal the lid.

2.   Cook on high pressure for 4 minutes.

3.   Allow pressure to release naturally then remove the lid and drain the greens and fish.

4.   In the mean time assemble fresh salads and veggies on a plate to make a bed for salmon and butternut squash cubes.

5.   Mix all ingredients for dressing in one bowl and use it to coat the salad once you place the salmon.

6.   Finally, add chopped chives and enjoy!

Recipe #45: Chicken Balance Bowl

In this super easy and extra tasty dish you will find a well balanced combination of proteins, vitamins, carbs and fibers along with everything else you need in your meal.

Yield: 1 serving

Prep: 10 minutes

Cook: 5 minutes

Time Taken: 15 minutes

Ingredients:

- 2 chicken breasts – cut into bite size cubes
- 2 cups of butternut squash - chopped
- Coconut oil – about 3 tablespoons in total
- 6 cups of greens - mixed
- 1 avocado - chopped
- 1 tablespoon of lemon juice
- 1 tablespoon of vinegar – apple cider
- 3 tablespoons of water
- salt
- pepper
- 2 teaspoons of garlic – powdered

Instructions:

1.   Turn Instant pot to Sauté and brown the chicken cubes with some coconut oil, salt and pepper. Add the butternut squash cubes once the chicken is browned then seal the lid and switch to Manual option.

2.   Cook on high pressure for 5 minutes.

3.   Next take water, pepper, salt, garlic, apple cider vinegar and lemon juice and whisk those ingredients together.

4.   Place the greens on the bottom of a bowl then pour the vinegar mixture over the greens.

5.   Top with butternut squash and chicken cubes.

Recipe #46: Mediterranean Beef Salad

This dish is inspired by Mediterranean cuisine and as such is refreshing and complimented with herbs and spices to resemble of rich Mediterranean cuisine. It's easy to make and light to eat.

Yield: 4 servings

Prep: 10 minutes

Cook: 15 minutes

Time Taken: 25 minutes

Ingredients:

For Dressing

- 2 lemons - juiced
- ¼ cup of oil - olive
- 1 lemon - zest
- 1 teaspoon of Herbs de Provence
- Pinch of red chili flakes
- 1 garlic clove - minced
- 1 sprig of rosemary
- 6 olives - pitted

Salad

- 500 g of beef – lean meat, steak
- 4 baby cucumbers – sliced
- 6 vine tomatoes – ripe, quartered
- 1 bell pepper – yellow, diced
- 1 bell pepper – red, diced
- ½ of onion – small, sliced
- Handful of parsley – chopped, fresh
- salt
- pepper

Instructions:

1. Sprinkle some olive oil into the bottom of your Instant pot and turn it on Sauté option.
2. Cut the steak into strips then add to the pot. Brown for a couple of minutes then seal the lid and switch to Meat option.
3. Cook on high pressure for 15 minutes.
4. Allow pressure to release naturally then open the lid.
5. Combine all veggies in one bowl then take all dressing ingredients and mix them all together. Dress the veggies then toss in the beef bits and stir to mix it all up.
6. Serve and enjoy!

Recipe #47: Cauliflower Rice

During Whole30 diet, rice is strictly prohibited, but luckily there is a healthy and nutritious substitute you can have for dinner – Cauliflower Rice.

Yield: 4 servings

Prep: 10 minutes

Cook: 3 minutes

Time Taken: 13 minutes

Ingredients:

- 1 head of cauliflower - processed to grain texture in food processor
- 1 cup of carrots - chopped
- 1 cup of celery - chopped
- 1 onion – small, chopped
- 4 garlic cloves - minced
- 4 tablespoons of sesame oil
- 2 eggs – large, beaten
- ¼ cup of cilantro – fresh, leaves
- ¼ cup of green onions
- Sesame seeds – black, for garnishing

Sauce

- ¼ cup of coconut aminos
- ½ tablespoon of arrowroot flour
- 2 tablespoons of cold water

Instructions:

1.   Turn your Instant pot to Sauté option and add some oil, celery, carrots and onion and cook until softened.

2.   Add the processed cauliflower then pour the beaten eggs and mix until combined.

3.   Seal the lid and set on Manual option, cooking on high pressure for 3 minutes

4.   You will then make a sauce by combining water and arrowroot flour then pour coconut aminos in a skillet then mix with arrowroot mixture and cook and stir until the sauce thickens.

5.   Combine the sauce with cauliflower rice and enjoy!

Recipe #48: Sweet Potato Pasta

You are not allowed to eat anything grain based so that means that you are also not allowed to eat pasta. But, what if pasta is made of sweet potatoes? Huge YES!

Yield: 2 servings

Prep: 10 minutes

Cook: 8 minutes

Time Taken: 18 minutes

Ingredients:

- 2 sweet potatoes - peeled and made in spirals with spiralizer
- 1 teaspoon of garlic - minced
- ¼ cup of onion - chopped
- 1 tablespoon of avocado oil
- pepper
- salt
- pinch of chili pepper flakes
- ½ cup of kale – fresh
- 1 can tomato sauce

Instructions:

1. Take Instant pot and fill it with water. Place the trivet and then place an insert bowl. Place the spiraled potatoes in the insert bowl.

2. Seal the lid and set on Manual setting, cooking on high pressure for 3 minutes.

3. Allow the pressure to release naturally then drain the water and set potato spaghetti aside.

4. Next you will add olive oil to your Instant pot and set it on Sauté option. Add garlic and onions. Cook until softened then add salt, pepper, chili flakes and kale.

5. Cook for another minute or two until kale gets softened then add tomato sauce and stir cook for minute longer.

6. Add potato spaghetti and cook for another minute mixing the potato pasta with the sauce.

7. Enjoy!

Recipe #49: Zucchini Noodles

We have had Whole30 pasta and now it's time for Whole30 compliant noodles. Try this amazing combination of flavors with zucchinis as noodles.

Yield: 2 servings

Prep: 5 minutes

Cook: 10 minutes

Time Taken: 15 minutes

Ingredients:

- 1 zucchini – large, spiraled with a spiralizer
- ½ of avocado
- ¼ cup of oil - olive
- 2 tablespoon of water
- 2 garlic cloves - minced
- 2 sweet potatoes - chopped
- 2 eggs
- 2 tablespoon of green onions - chopped
- Salt
- Pepper

Instructions:

1.   You will first make avocado cream by combining avocado, garlic, water and 2 tablespoons of olive oil into a food processor and blending the mixture until smooth.

2.   Add olive oil to the Instant pot then add cubed potatoes and sprinkle with salt and pepper then break the eggs on top and add some more salt and pepper.

3.   Seal the lid and set on Manual, cooking on high pressure for 10 minutes.

4.   Allow the pressure to release naturally then open the lid.

5.   Combine avocado paste with zucchini noodles and set them on a plate.

6.   Place potatoes with eggs on top.

7.   Garnish with chopped green onions.

Recipe #50: Mushroom Bowl with Cauliflower Rice

Mushrooms are super tasty and an awesome source of protein. The best of all, mushrooms are Whole30 compliant!

Yield: 4 servings

Prep: 10 minutes

Cook: 5 minutes

Time Taken: 15 minutes

Ingredients:

- 6 cups of processed cauliflower florets – made to look like rice, grainy texture
- 2 tablespoons of oil - olive
- Salt
- pepper
- 3 cups of mushrooms - cremini
- 2 teaspoons of garlic - minced
- 8 cups of baby spinach

Instructions:

1. Take olive oil and toss it in the Instant pot then turn the pot on Sauté option. Add mushrooms, salt, pepper and garlic and sauté until the mushrooms are softened then add spinach and cauliflower and another spoon of olive oil then seal the lid.

2. Set the pot on Manual and cook for 3 minutes on high pressure.

3. Allow the pressure to release naturally then serve and enjoy!

Recipe #51: Orange Chicken

If you have had a light lunch, then you will enjoy this nutritious flavor packed meal with chicken bits soaked in orange sauce.

Yield: 2 servings

Prep: 10 minutes

Cook: 5 minutes

Time Taken: 15 minutes

Ingredients:

- ¾ cup of orange juice – 100% clean
- 1 orange – medium, zest only
- 1 tablespoon of coconut aminos
- 1 teaspoon of vinegar - rice
- Pinch of chili flakes
- Salt
- pepper
- ½ tablespoon of avocado oil
- ½ tablespoon of ginger – fresh, minced
- 1 teaspoon of garlic - minced
- 1 teaspoon of tapioca

For the chicken

- 2 tablespoon of avocado oil
- 3 tablespoons of tapioca starch
- Salt
- pepper
- 200 g chicken breasts – cubed, boneless, no skin

Instructions:

1. First, you will make a sauce by whisking together orange juice, coconut aminos, zest, rice vinegar, salt, pepper and chili flakes.
2. Turn your Instant pot to Sauté option then add garlic, ginger and some oil.
3. When ginger and garlic change the color, add the mixture from the bowl, and let it simmer on Sauté.
4. Add tapioca starch and stir it in well.
5. Cook until the sauce is glossy and thickened.
6. Take care of the chicken cubes by mixing together salt, pepper and tapioca starch in a bag then add the cubes in the bag.
7. Mix it up all well until the cubes are coated.
8. Add the chicken bits to the pot with the sauce and seal the lid.
9. Set on Poultry option and cook on high pressure for 5 minutes.
10. Allow the pressure to release naturally and remove the lid.
11. Serve with cauliflower rice and enjoy!

Recipe #52: Taco Bowl

We have had a Taco Soup and now it's time to turn this amazing Mexican dish into a Whole30 bowl that will shush your taco cravings.

Yield: 2 servings

Prep: 10 minutes

Cook: 10 minutes

Time Taken: 20 minutes

Ingredients:

- 4 cups of green salad mix
- Lettuce – 4 or 5 pieces
- 500 g of turkey – ground
- 1 onion – small, chopped
- 5 garlic cloves – minced
- 2 cups of cherry tomatoes – halved
- Hot sauce - per taste
- 1 cup of tomato paste
- Salt
- Pepper
- Chili flakes
- Olive oil

Instructions:

1. First you will take lettuce and green salad mix and place it in a bowl for serving – you have enough for two servings.
2. Sprinkle the salads with some salt and olive or coconut oil.
3. Turn your Instant pot on Sauté option. Add the ground meat, breaking it in bits while stirring then add garlic and onions. Cook together until onions are softened and the turkey is browned.
4. Sprinkle with salt and pepper, chili flakes and add hot sauce. Stir in tomato paste.
5. Seal the lid and set on Poultry option. Cook on high pressure for 5 minutes.
6. Quick release and open the lid.
7. Mix the meat with halved cherry tomatoes then use this filling to fill up the bowls bedded with salads.
8. Enjoy!

Recipe #53: Garlic Potato Roast

This meal can easily be mixed up for tasty Italian bruschette – only it's completely Whole30 and compliant so you can enjoy it without feeling guilty.

Yield: 6 servings

Prep: 10 minutes

Cook: 10 minutes

Time Taken: 20 minutes

Ingredients:

- 1 kg of potatoes – baby red
- 3 tablespoons of avocado butter
- 2 teaspoon of dill - dry
- 1 teaspoon of parsley - dry
- 1 teaspoon of garlic - powdered
- ½ teaspoon of onion – powdered
- Sea salt
- Pepper

Instructions:

1. Whisk everything except from baby potatoes, together, and pour into an insert dish for Instant pot. Pour a glass of water at the bottom of the pot.

2. Cut potatoes in halves and arrange the cut parts down across the mixture in the dish.

3. Seal the lid and set on Manual option, cooking on high pressure for 10 minutes.

4. Allow the pressure to release naturally.

5. Once warm, you can cut potatoes in slices and serve as bruschette with your sauce of choice.

Recipe #54: Mini Pizzas

No, you are still not allowed to have pizza during Whole30 program, but here is a healthy and equally tasty substitute you can indulge in.

Yield: 4 servings

Prep: 10 minutes

Cook: 10 minutes

Time Taken: 20 minutes

Ingredients:

- 4 potatoes - russet
- 8 tablespoons of sauce for pizza
- 4 Italian sausage links – browned and removed from casings
- 30 slices of pepperoni – browned, crisped
- 2 cups of mushrooms - sautéed
- garlic cloves – 5 pieces, minced
- oregano

Instructions:

1.   Turn on your Instant pot on Sauté option and brown the pepperoni and Italian sausage – brown Italian sausage with garlic then add mushrooms and pizza sauce in the end. Cook all together for about 5-8 minutes.

2.   Once cool, cut the potatoes in half and spoon the meat out, saving the skin.

3.   Take the halved potatoes and scrape some of the insides leaving the skin and some of the "meat".

4.   Fill the potatoes with the mixture you have made, sprinkle oregano on all potatoes and place them in the insert dish.

5.   Set the dish on a trivet and pour one cup of water into the Instant pot.

6.   Seal the lid and set on Manual setting, cooking on high pressure for 10 minutes.

7.   Allow the pressure to release naturally then remove the insert dish.

8.   Serve and enjoy!

Recipe #55: Shredded Turkey and Greens Salad

This salad is packed with vitamins, fibers and calcium and would make for a perfect dinner – and as a great plus, it will only take you a couple of minutes.

Yield: 4 servings

Prep: 5 minutes

Cook: 5 minutes

Time Taken: 10 minutes

Ingredients:

- 2 turkey breasts
- 1 cup of water
- 4 cups of kale - chopped
- 4 cups of brussel sprouts - shredded
- ½ cup of cranberries - dry
- 2 lemons - juiced
- 2 tablespoons of oil - olive
- 1 tablespoon of mustard – sugar free
- salt
- pepper

Instructions:

1. Take a bowl and whisk lemon juice, salt, pepper, olive oil and mustard together.

2. Mix up all the greens in a bowl then dress them with the mixture you have made. Add cranberries and stir it all up well.

3. Take your Instant pot and place the turkey breasts and pour the water over it, adding salt and pepper.

4. Seal the lid and set on Poultry option. Cook on high pressure for 10 minutes.

5. Drain the meat and shred it with a fork then add it to the bowl.

6. Enjoy!

Recipe #56: Detox Salad

This salad will surely provide your body with needed balance! Check out the ingredient list and get on it!

Yield: 6 servings

Prep: 10 minutes

Cook: 15 minutes

Time Taken: 25 minutes

Ingredients:

Dressing

- 1/3 cup of oil - grape seed
- ½ cup of lemon juice -freshly squeezed
- 1 tablespoon of ginger – fresh, grated
- 2 teaspoons of mustard – whole grain, sugar free
- Salt – to taste

For salad

- 2 chicken breasts
- 1 cup of water
- 2 cups of kale
- 2 cups of cabbage – red, sliced in thin slices
- 2 cups of broccoli – florets only, chopped
- 2 carrots – large, grated
- 1 bell pepper – red, cut into sticks
- 2 avocados - diced
- ½ cup of parsley – fresh, chopped
- 1 tablespoon of sesame seeds

Instructions:

1. Either put the dressing ingredients through a food processor or whisk them until smooth.
2. Take all salad ingredients except from parsley, avocados and sesame seeds and place those in a bowl, mixing everything well.
3. Place the chicken breast into the Instant pot with a cup of water and add some salt and pepper.
4. Seal the lid and set on Poultry option. Cook for 10 minutes on high pressure.
5. Drain the water and shred the chicken with a fork.
6. Add chicken to the bowl.
7. Dress the salad mixture with the dressing you have made then top with avocados, parsley and sesame seeds.
8. Enjoy!

Recipe #57: Egg Role in a Bowl

This delicious meal will surely silence your cravings for something creamy and nutritious.

Yield: 4 servings

Prep: 5 minutes

Cook: 10 minutes

Time Taken: 15 minutes

Ingredients:

- 2 tablespoons of oil - sesame
- 6 green onions - sliced, divide green parts from white parts
- ½ cup of onion – red, diced
- 5 garlic cloves - minced
- 500 g of pork - ground
- 1 teaspoon of ginger – fresh, grated
- 2 tablespoons of hit sauce – use Whole30 compliant version – low sodium, sugar free
- 4 cups of coleslaw mix
- 3 tablespoons of coconut aminos
- 1 tablespoon of vinegar - rice
- White pepper – pinch
- Salt
- Black sesame seeds – for garnishing

Instructions:

1. Turn your Instant pot to Sauté option then add some oil, garlic, white parts of green onion and red onions. Sauté until softened.

2. Next you will add ginger, chili sauce and ground meat. Sauté until browned

3. Add coconut aminos, vinegar, salt, white paper and coleslaw mix then stir in and cook until tender.

4. Mix it all together then serve with green parts of green onions and sesame on top.

Recipe #58: Steakhouse Salad

This light meal is a complete dinner with all the veggies you need, all complimented with fresh stake. Try it out and see it for yourself!

Yield: 4 servings

Prep: 5 minutes

Cook: 10 minutes

Time Taken: 15 minutes

Ingredients:

- 300 g of steak - sirloin
- 3 tablespoons of Cajun seasoning – make sure it's compliant
- 2 tablespoons *of avocado butter*

Salad

- 1 head lettuce – small, romaine, sliced
- 1 tomato - sliced
- 1 cucumber - diced
- 8 eggs - cooked to be soft or hardboiled – to your taste
- ¼ cup of olives - pitted
- 2 avocados – ripe, peeled
- Ranch dressing – in case you can find Whole30 compliant

Instructions:

1. Assemble all the salads in one bowl and set aside.
2. Add avocado butter to your Instant pot and coat the steak with Cajun seasoning.
3. Set the Instant pot on Sauté option and brown the steak on all sides, 2-3 minutes per one side.
4. Seal the lid and set on Meat option. Cook for 20 minutes on high pressure.
5. Allow the pressure to release naturally then open the lid.
6. Slice the steak then add it to the salad. Add salt to the salad if needed and dress it with ranch dressing in case you have a compliant one.

Recipe #59: Cabbage and Chicken Stir Fry

This combination will make you crave for more and it is only made in 15 minutes all cooking included.

Yield: 4 servings

Prep: 5 minutes

Cook: 15 minutes

Time Taken: 20 minutes

Ingredients:

- 2 tablespoons of oil – olive
- 3 garlic cloves - minced
- 1 onion – yellow, medium, diced
- 500 g of chicken breasts – cut in cubes, boneless, no skin
- 5 cups of cabbage - shredded
- ½ bell pepper – large, chopped
- ¼ cup of coconut aminos
- ½ teaspoon of ginger - ground
- salt
- pepper
- 2 tablespoon of chives - chopped

Instructions:

1. Set your Instant pot to Sauté option and add garlic and onions – sauté until browned and softened.

2. Next you will add the chicken cubes and cook it until it is browned on all sides.

3. Add shredded cabbage along with the rest of the ingredients except for chives.

4. Seal the lid and set the Instant Pot on Manual setting, cooking on high pressure for 10 minutes.

5. Allow the pressure to release naturally then open the lid.

6. Garnish with chives and enjoy!

Recipe #60: Spaghetti Squash with Chicken

Another dish created as a substitute for pasta. This time we are in for a version, complimented with chicken bits.

Yield: 4 servings

Prep: 5 minutes

Cook: 25 minutes

Time Taken: 30 minutes

Ingredients:

- 2 cups of kale - chopped
- ¾ cups of Caesar dressing – Whole30 compliant
- 1 Spaghetti squash
- 1 chicken breast - large
- salt
- pepper

Instructions:

1. Take kale and place it in a bowl, mixing it with the dressing and pressing so that kale is soaked.

2. Take a trivet and place it in the Instant pot, also pouring one cup of water at the bottom.

3. Pierce a couple of holes into the squash before placing it on the trivet.

4. Seal the lid and cook on Manual setting, cooking on high pressure for 15 minutes.

5. Allow the pressure to release naturally then open the lid.

6. Halve the squash and scrape the "meat" with a fork, creating spaghettis.

7. Clean the pot then add some oil to the Instant pot, turn on Sauté option then add the chicken breast and brown it on both sides. Lock the lid and set on Poultry option. Cook for 10 minutes on high pressure.

8. Allow the pressure to release naturally then take the chicken out and cut it into strips.

9. Add spaghettis and chicken to the kale bowl.

10. Serve and enjoy!

Recipe #61: Asparagus and Chicken Skillet with Sweet Potatoes

The title says it all – no surprise there, but you will be surprised by how easy this meal is to prepare. More surprise will come with the first bite and it won't stop there!

Yield: 4 servings

Prep: 5 minutes

Cook: 15 minutes

Time Taken: 20 minutes

Ingredients:

- 500 g of chicken breasts – cubed, boneless, no skin
- 1 tablespoon of oil - olive
- Salt
- pepper
- 3 garlic cloves - minced
- 1 sweet potato – medium, peeled, diced
- ½ cup of broth – chicken, you can also use water instead
- 200 g of asparagus – fresh, halved
- ½ teaspoon of red pepper – crushed

Instructions:

1. Season the chicken cubes with salt and pepper then add it to the Instant pot and turn to Sauté option. Brown the chicken and add garlic. Sauté until the garlic is mildly browned as well.

2. Add potatoes, broth, asparagus and red pepper then set on Manual cooking and seal the lid. Cook for 10 minutes on high pressure.

3. Allow the pressure to release naturally then open the lid.

4. Serve and enjoy!

Recipe #62: Sausage Egg Stuffed Meatballs

These meatballs are super tasty and Whole30 compliant, so this delish is set to become a regular meal on your dinner menu.

Yield: 4 servings

Prep: 5 minutes

Cook: 10 minutes

Time Taken: 15 minutes

Ingredients:

- 500 g of Italian sausage
- 8 eggs – hard boiled, peeled
- Salt
- Pepper
- 4 garlic cloves
- 1 onion – small, diced
- Olive oil

Instructions:

1. Remove the meat from the sausage casings and set aside.

2. Combine chopped parsley, onions and minced garlic with the meat, making a mixture then make balls out of it – there should be 8 balls.

3. Make patties out of those balls and place one boiled and peeled egg on each patty then roll it into making a stuffed meatball.

4. Set your Instant pot on Sauté, add the oil and fry the meatballs on all sides for 2 minutes or so.

5. Seal the lid and set on Manual, cooking on high pressure for 10 minutes.

6. Quick release the pressure and open the lid.

7. Have these super tasty meatballs with salad mix or with a sauce of your choice.

Recipe #63: Mustard Chicken with Garlic

If you still haven't tried the amazing combination of garlic and mustard by now, you definitely should. It goes great with meat, especially poultry!

Yield: 6 servings

Prep: 5 minutes

Cook: 15 minutes

Time Taken: 20 minutes

Ingredients:

- 700 g of chicken breasts – boneless, no skin
- ½ cup of mustard – brown, spicy, sugar free
- ½ cup of oil - olive
- 2 teaspoons of garlic – finely minced

Instructions:

1. Take the olive oil, garlic and mustard and whisk it in a bowl. Place the chicken into the bowl and let it soak in mustard. The best is to do this the night before and let the chicken rest in the marinade for an entire day.

2. Take the chicken parts and set on the bottom of greased Instant pot. Seal the lid and set on Poultry option. Cook for 10 minutes on high pressure.

3. Allow the pressure to release naturally then open the lid.

4. Serve and enjoy!

CHAPTER 5: WHOLE30 PROGRAM SNACK RECIPES

Snacks are as important as the main courses and instead of snacking on chips, tortillas and other overly processed food, you will be making fast and healthy snacks that are Whole30 compliant. To make your snack time as pleasant as possible, we have compiled this interesting, healthy and tasty list of snack recipes you can make with help of your Instant pot.

Recipe #64: Monkey Salad

This salad is complimented with different nutty flavors, upgraded with fruity splash that will surely get you full until lunch time.

Yield: 1 serving

Prep: 5 minutes

Cook: 3 minutes

Time Taken: 8 minutes

Ingredients:

- 1 banana - sliced
- ¼ cup of blueberries
- ¼ cup of cashews - raw
- 1 tablespoon of almond butter
- Pinch of cinnamon - powdered
- Coconut flakes
- 1 cup of coconut milk

Instructions:

1. Slice the banana and place it on the bottom of a small bowl then add the cashews and blueberries.

2. Top with almond butter then add the mixture to the Instant pot along with coconut milk.

3. Seal the lid and set on Manual, cooking on high pressure for 3 minutes.

4. Quick release, then open the lid.

5. Pour into a bowl and top it with coconut flakes.

6. Enjoy!

Recipe #65: Cranberry and Coconut Energy Bars

You don't need to spend your money or time looking for snack bars that are Whole30 compliant and often expensive – we are presenting an interesting, cheap and tasty recipe so you can make your own energy bars!

Yield: 8 servings

Prep: 10 minutes

Cook: 10 minutes

Time Taken: 20 minutes

Ingredients:

- 1 cup of dates - pitted
- 2 cups of walnuts
- 2 cups of coconut - desiccated
- ¾ cup of cranberries - dry
- 3 tablespoons of water

Instructions:

1. Preheat the oven and take a baking pan placing the walnuts onto the pan. Roast the walnuts for about 10 minutes.

2. Take the water, dates, coconut, cranberries and roasted walnuts and put it all in a food processor.

3. Blend until smooth and mixed all well.

4. Incorporate the mixture onto the insert dish of the Instant pot.

5. Pour one cup of water into the pot then seal the lid and set in high pressure, choosing Manual option for cooking. Cook for 5 minutes.

6. Quick release, then open the lid.

7. Place the cooked mixture into the fridge and let it cool for a couple of hours.

8. Cut in bars and serve.

9. You can store these bars for days in the fridge.

Recipe #66: Kale "Chips"

Can't snack on chips? No big deal as we have just the right thing for you – this kale chips is easy to make and it comes with pizza flavor. Let's see how you can make it.

Yield: 10 servings

Prep: 5 minutes

Cook: 5 minutes

Time Taken: 10 minutes

Ingredients:

- 1 bunch of kale – large bunch
- 2 cups of cashews – raw, soaked
- ⅔ cup of roasted peppers – jarred, you will also need 3 tablespoons of its juice
- ⅓ cup of nutritional yeast
- 3 tablespoons of oil - olive
- 1 lemon - juiced
- 1 teaspoon of Italian seasoning
- ½ teaspoon of garlic - powdered
- ¼ teaspoon of chili – powdered
- Salt
- Pepper

Instructions:

1. Take kale and dry it if too wet – use pat drying. Place kale in a bowl.

2. Take all the ingredients except for kale and put them in the food processor. Blend until smooth.

3. Take the sauce mixture and pour over kale. Mix it all up well so kale is coated then spread evenly across the insert dish.

4. Place the dish on the trivet.

5. Seal the lid and set on Manual, cooking on high pressure for 5 minutes.

Recipe #67: Fruit Cream

If you are aching for something sweet and fruity this snack recipe will come as ordered. Try it out and you are guaranteed to make it more than once.

Yield: 1 serving

Prep: 5 minutes

Cook: 5 minutes

Time Taken: 10 minutes

Ingredients:

- 1 cup of coconut cream – full fat
- ½ cup of strawberries – diced
- ½ cup of blueberries
- ½ cup of raspberries
- ½ cup of apples – diced, unpeeled

Instructions:

1. The recipe is pretty simple as you only need to cut all the fruits as described and mix them all up.

2. Pour coconut cream over the fruits then stir to coat the fruits the pour the mixture into a ramekin.

3. Place the ramekin onto a trivet and pour one cup of water into the pot.

4. Seal the lid and set on Manual, cooking on high pressure for 5 minutes.

5. Quick release and open the lid.

6. You can garnish with coconut flakes.

Recipe #68: Creamy Fruit Bowl

Another interesting fruity flavored combination you can have as a snack and make it in no time.

Yield: 1 serving

Prep: 5 minutes

Cook: 5 minutes

Time Taken: 10 minutes

Ingredients:

- 1 banana – large, sliced
- 1 apple – large, sweet, wedged
- 1 cup of coconut flakes – roasted
- 2 tablespoons of almond butter
- ½ cup of raspberries

Instructions:

1. Take the butter and coconut flakes and place them together in the instant pot.

2. Seal the lid and set on Manual, cooking on high pressure for 5 minutes.

3. Quick release the pressure and remove lid.

4. Arrange apples, banana and raspberries in a bowl mixing them altogether then top it with almond butter and coconut flakes.

5. Enjoy!

Recipe #69: Faux Sushi Avocado Bites

This snack is inspired by everyone's favorite take out – sushi. The only thing we have saved from the original sushi recipe is wasabi sauce and seaweed.

Yield: 1 serving

Prep: 5 minutes

Cook: 3 minutes

Time Taken: 8 minutes

Ingredients:

- 4 pieces of seaweed ready for sushi making
- 1 carrot – grated
- Sesame seeds
- Wasabi sauce
- Half of avocado – sliced

Instructions:

1. Assemble the seaweed then arrange the toppings in the following order.

2. First you will place a slice of avocado on each seaweed piece then you will add some grated salted carrots.

3. Place in the insert dish and set the dish on the trivet.

4. Pour a cup of water into the Instant pot then seal the lid.

5. Set on Manual option and cook for 3 minutes on high pressure.

6. Quick release then open the lid.

7. Next add a splash of wasabi on top of each seaweed and over the carrots, then sprinkle with sesame seeds.

8. Enjoy!

Recipe #70: Broccoli and Potato Vinegar Salad

Unlike creamy dinner salads starring many different ingredients into making a whole course that could make up for a meal, for snack you can have this light but nutritious hearty salad with potatoes and broccoli.

Yield: 4 servings

 Prep: 5 minutes

Cook: 10 minutes

Time Taken: 15 minutes

Ingredients:

- 500 g of potatoes – baby red, peeled, halved
- 500 g of broccoli – florets, bigger chunks
- Salt
- Pepper
- 3 tablespoons of apple cider vinegar
- Parsley – fresh, chopped

Instructions:

1. Take the halved potatoes and broccoli florets and place them on the trivet. Pour a cup of water into the Instant pot and seal the lid.

2. Set on Manual, cooking on high pressure for 8 minutes.

3. Quick release the pressure and remove the trivet with veggies.

4. Place the veggies into a bowl then splash with vinegar, salt and pepper.

5. Garnish with parsley and dig in!

Recipe #71: Trail Mix with Coconut Yogurt

You can make your own trail mix to snack on in no time – just check out the ingredient list, hit the store and assemble your own trail mix and top it with homemade Instant pot coconut yoghurt.

Yield: 1 serving (there will be leftover coconut yoghurt)

Prep: 5 minutes

Cook: 8 hours

Time Taken: 8 hours 5 minutes

Ingredients:

- ¼ cup of almonds
- ¼ cup of cashews – roasted
- ¼ cup of cranberries – dry
- ¼ cup of walnuts
- 1/8 cup of coconut flakes
- 1 pack of vegan yogurt starter
- 1 tablespoon of gelatin
- 2 cans of coconut milk

Instructions:

1. Assemble all nuts in a mason jar and set aside.

2. In the meantime, pour the coconut cream into the liner of the Instant pot and set on Yogurt option then press adjust. This will bring the cream to simmer.

3. Let it cool to 100 F - you can't allow it to get too cool or leave it too hot.

4. Next you will whisk in the yogurt starter until the lumps are gone.

5. Set on Yogurt option again and set the timer to 8 hours.

6. Once it's done and warm, stir in the gelatin.

7. Pour some of the yogurt into the Trail Mix jar and enjoy!

Recipe #72: Coconut Berry Yogurt

Another Coconut yogurt delight – this time we are snacking on berries complimented with this Instant pot wonder.

Yield: 1 serving (there will be leftover coconut yogurt)

Prep: 5 minutes

Cook: 8 hours

Time Taken: 8 hours 5 minutes

Ingredients:

- 2 cans of coconut cream
- 1 pack of vegan yogurt starter
- 1 tablespoon of gelatin
- ½ cup of strawberries
- ½ cup of blueberries

Instructions:

1. In case you have coconut yogurt leftovers, use that for this recipe and in case you have to start from scratch, here is how you can make it.

2. Pour the coconut cream into the liner of the Instant pot and set on Yogurt option then press adjust. This will bring the cream to simmer.

3. Let it cool to 100 F - you can't allow it to get too cool or leave it too hot.

4. Next you will whisk in the yogurt starter until the lumps are gone.

5. Set on Yogurt option again and set the timer to 8 hours.

6. Once it's done and warm, stir in the gelatin.

7. Add berries to the serving bowl and add some coconut yogurt. Mix it up and enjoy!

Recipe #73: Pumpkin spice and Lemon Zest Mug Cake

This easy to make mug cakes are perfect for snacking and you can make these easily with your instant pot.

Yield: 1 serving

Prep: 5 minutes

Cook: 10 minutes

Time Taken: 15 minutes

Ingredients:

- 1/3 cup of almond flour
- 1/8 teaspoon of vanilla extract
- Pinch of salt
- 1 egg
- Coconut oil for greasing up the mason jar
- 1 teaspoon of pumpkin spice
- 1 lemon – zest only

Instructions:

1. Take all the ingredients and whisk them together. Pour the mixture in a heat-proof mason jar and seal it with aluminum foil.

2. Place the jar on the trivet and pour one cup of water into the pot.

3. Seal the lid and set on Manual, cooking on high pressure for 10 minutes.

4. Quick release the pressure and open the lid once the pot is cool.

5. Serve and enjoy!

Recipe #74: Coconut Berry Jar Cake

Another perfect snack to keep you going! Try this amazingly delicious coconut and berry combination!

Yield: 1 serving

Prep: 5 minutes

Cook: 10 minutes

Time Taken: 15 minutes

Ingredients:

- ½ cup of mixed berries – raspberries, blueberries, blackberries
- 1/3 cup of almond flour
- 1/8 teaspoon of vanilla extract
- Pinch of salt
- 1 egg
- Coconut oil for greasing up the mason jar

Instructions:

1. Whisk all the ingredients together in a bowl then add the berry mix and combine it well with the egg mixture.

2. Grease up a mason jar then pour the mixture into the jar.

3. Place a trivet and add a cup of water into the Instant pot.

4. Set the pot on Manual and place the jar onto the trivet.

5. Seal the lid and cook for 10 minutes.

6. Quick release the pressure, then open the lid.

7. Serve and enjoy!

Recipe #75: Mini Peach Cobbler

Cobblers are just the best, so we made a healthy Whole30 recipe for all of you who are in love with peach cobbler.

Yield: 1 serving

Prep: 5 minutes

Cook: 10 minutes

Time Taken: 15 minutes

Ingredients:

- 1/3 cup of almond flour
- 2 peaches – large, peeled, diced
- 1/8 teaspoon of vanilla extract
- Pinch of salt
- 1 egg
- Coconut oil for greasing up the ramekin

Instructions:

1.   Take all the ingredients except for peaches and whisk them in a bowl. Then add the peaches and combine until well mixed.

2.   Pour the mixture into a small ramekin and place it on the trivet that you have previously set in the Instant pot.

3.   Pour a cup of water to the bottom of the pot and seal the lid.

4.   Cook on Manual setting, high pressure, setting the timer on 10 minutes.

5.   Quick release the pressure and remove the lid.

6.   Serve and enjoy!

Recipe #76: Cocoa and Nut Jar Cake

Another great recipe for another great snack – this time we are making a no flour cake with cocoa powder and nuts.

Yield: 1 serving

Prep: 5 minutes

Cook: 10 minutes

Time Taken: 15 minutes

Ingredients:

- 1/3 cup of almond flour
- 2 tablespoons of cocoa powder – unsweetened
- ½ cup of mixed nuts – nuts of your choice
- 1/8 teaspoon of vanilla extract
- Pinch of salt
- 1 egg
- Coconut oil for greasing up the ramekin

Instructions:

1. Take all the ingredients except for nuts and whisk them in a bowl.
2. Take the nuts and blend them in your food processor until the mix gets a flour like texture.
3. Combine nuts with the egg mixture and mix it until well blended.
4. Pour the mixture into a ramekin and set the trivet in your Instant pot.
5. Pour a cup of water and seal the lid.
6. Set the pot on Manual function, cooking on high pressure for 10 minutes.
7. Quick release the pressure and remove the lid.
8. Serve and enjoy!

Recipe #77: Spicy Roasted Nuts

These finely roasted nuts will surely get you through the day until you sit down and have a decent meal for lunch. Spiced up and complimented with rosemary, these nuts will make you go nuts (tastes so good!)!

Yield: 4 servings

Prep: 5 minutes

Cook: 15 minutes

Time Taken: 20 minutes

Ingredients:

- 2 cups of cashew, pistachio and almond mix
- 2 cups of jumbo nature cashews
- 1 ½ tablespoons of oil - avocado
- 1 ½ teaspoon of chili - powdered
- ½ teaspoon of cumin - ground
- ½ lime - juiced
- 1 tablespoon of rosemary – chopped, fresh

Instructions:

1. Take lime juice, cumin, chili, rosemary and avocado oil and whisk them in one bowl.
2. Place the nuts onto the insert dish and pour one cup of water into the Instant pot.
3. Pour over nuts and stir to coat them then spread equally across the dish.
4. Seal the lid and set on Manual. Cook for 15 minutes on high pressure.
5. Quick release and enjoy!
6. Enjoy!

Recipe #78: Banana Bread

Banana bread the way we make it is a great snack when on healthy Whole30 diet, but instead of buying it, you can now easily make it at home

Yield: 6 servings

Prep: 10 minutes

Cook: 10 minutes

Time Taken: 20 minutes

Ingredients:

- 10 bananas – ripe, but not mushy
- 1 lemon – juiced
- 1/3 cup of almond flour
- 1/8 teaspoon of vanilla extract
- Pinch of salt
- 1 egg
- Coconut oil for greasing up the dish

Instructions:

1. Take the bananas and mash them then take the rest of the ingredients and mix them all up, whisking and stirring until smooth. You can also use your food processor.

2. Spread the mixture evenly across the insert dish you have previously greased up then place the dish onto the trivet.

3. Pour one cup of water into the bottom of your Instant pot then seal the lid and set on Manual.

4. Cook on high pressure for 10 minutes.

5. Quick release the pressure and remove the lid once the pot is cool.

6. Enjoy!

Recipe #79: Apple Cinnamon Ramekin Pie

Another sweet and delightful snack in form of one of the favorite family treats – apple pie! This time we are making our Instant Pot Whole30 version.

Yield: 1 serving

Prep: 5 minutes

Cook: 10 minutes

Time Taken: 15 minutes

Ingredients:

- 1/3 cup of almond flour
- 1/8 teaspoon of vanilla extract
- Pinch of salt
- 1 egg
- 1 cup of diced and peeled apples
- 1 teaspoon of cinnamon - ground
- Coconut oil for greasing up the mason jar

Instructions:

1. Take all the ingredients except for apples and whisk them in a bowl. Add the apples and combine with the egg mixture.

2. Pour the mixture into a greased up ramekin and place it on the trivet in your Instant pot.

3. Pour a cup of water into the pot and seal the lid.

4. Set on Manual option, cooking on high pressure for 10 minutes.

5. Quick release the pressure, then remove the lid.

6. Let the pie cool and then serve and enjoy!

Recipe #80: Stuffed Eggs

Another one of egg delish meals, this time in form of a snack – this is a light version of deviled eggs, topped with Whole30 compliant ingredients.

Yield: 2 servings

Prep: 10 minutes

Cook: 10 minutes

Time Taken: 20 minutes

Ingredients:

- 8 eggs – hard boiled
- 1 cup of pesto sauce
- 6 slices of bacon
- Olive oil

For pesto

- 1 cup of basil – fresh, leaves
- 3 garlic cloves
- 3 tablespoons of pine nuts
- Kosher salt
- pepper
- 1/3 cup of oil – olive

Instructions:

1. First you will make pesto by placing all pesto ingredients into a food processor. Blend all until smooth then place in a jar.

2. You will cook the eggs by pouring one cup of water into the Instant pot and placing the trivet in the Instant pot. Place the eggs onto the trivet.

3. Seal the lid and set on Manual and cook on high pressure for 5 minutes.

4. Allow the pressure to release naturally then remove the eggs.

5. Peel and halve the eggs.

6. Take the yolks out and mash them. Add pesto to the mashed yolks.

7. Clean the pot then set on Sauté. Sauté the bacon on some oil or in its own fat. Cook until crispy then crumble.

8. Mix the bacon with the pesto mixture then fill the eggs and serve!

9. Enjoy!

Recipe #81: Plantain Salsa Bread

This interesting combination would make even more interesting snack for busy days when you have only a couple of minutes to come up with something delicious to snack on.

Yield: 2 servings

Prep: 5 minutes

Cook: 10 minutes

Time Taken: 15 minutes

Ingredients:

- 2 tablespoon of oil - coconut
- 1 plantain – whole, green or ripe
- Salt - to taste
- 1/2 cup of almond flour
- Pinch of salt
- 2 eggs
- 1 cup of salsa sauce
- Coconut oil for greasing up the mason jar

Instructions:

1. Take the plantain then mash it with a fork. Mix it up with the rest of the ingredients except for salsa. Mix until smooth and combined – you can also use your food processor.

2. Then add salsa and whisk it up well.

3. Take the insert dish for your Instant pot and pour the mixture in, spreading it evenly.

4. Seal the lid and set on Manual function. Cook on high pressure for 10 minutes

5. Allow the pressure to release naturally then remove the lid.

6. Serve and enjoy!

Recipe #82: Sweet Potato Baked Fries

Although you are not allowed to have French fries here is a healthy alternative you can snack on!

Yield: 4 servings

Prep: 10 minutes

Cook: 10 minutes

Time Taken: 20 minutes

Ingredients:

- 3 sweet potatoes - medium
- 5 tablespoons of oil - olive
- 2 ½ tablespoons of cumin - ground
- 1 teaspoon of garlic - powdered
- Sea salt
- ½ teaspoon of chili - powdered
- Pepper

Instructions:

1. Cut the potatoes into sticks then coat them with spices and oil.

2. Spread evenly across the insert dish and place the dish onto the trivet. Pour a cup of water into the Instant pot.

3. Seal the lid and set on Manual cooking.

4. Cook on high pressure for 10 minutes.

5. Serve and enjoy! You can use dipping of your choice.

Recipe #83: Chocolate Munchkin

Yum! This chocolate delight is made to be Whole30 compliant and is easily prepared with your Instant Pot!

Yield: 1 serving

Prep: 5 minutes

Cook: 10 minutes

Time Taken: 15 minutes

Ingredients:

- 1/3 cup of almond flour
- 2 tablespoons of chocolate protein powder
- 1 tablespoon of almond butter
- 1 teaspoon of cocoa powder
- 1/8 teaspoon of vanilla extract
- Pinch of salt
- 1 egg
- Coconut oil for greasing up the mason jar

Instructions:

1. Take all ingredients and whisk them in a bowl, one by one, starting with the egg and butter.

2. Pour the mixture into a greased up ramekin then place it on the trivet in your Instant pot.

3. Pour a cup of water into the Instant pot then seal the lid and set on Manual functions.

4. Cook for 10 minutes on high pressure.

5. Quick release the pressure and remove the lid once the pot is cool.

6. Serve and enjoy!

Recipe #84: Chocolate Chip No Flour Cake

We have saved a special snack treat for the last recipe in our Instant Pot Whole30 cookbook – chocolate chip cake with no flour and with Whole30 compliant ingredients.

Yield: 1 serving

Prep: 5 minutes

Cook: 10 minutes

Time Taken: 15 minutes

Ingredients:

- 1 tablespoon of chocolate protein powder – unsweetened
- ½ cup of chocolate chips - dark chocolate, unsweetened
- 1/3 cup of almond flour
- 1 teaspoon of cocoa powder
- 1/8 teaspoon of vanilla extract
- Pinch of salt
- 1 egg
- Coconut oil for greasing up the mason jar

Instructions:

1. Take all ingredients except for chocolate chips and whisk them together. Add chocolate chips to the mixture but leave a couple for the end.

2. Pour the mixture in to a ramekin then place the ramekin on the trivet set in your Instant pot.

3. Top the mixture in the ramekin with the remaining chocolate chips.

4. Pour a cup of water into the Instant pot and seal the lid.

5. Cook on Manual function for 10 minutes, cooking on high pressure.

6. Quick release the pressure and remove the lid.

7. Serve and enjoy!

CHAPTER 6: 14-DAY WHOLE30 MEAL PLAN

To help you find your way around with your new Whole30 program, we have assembled a 14-day meal plan that will include the recipes from our Whole30 Program Cookbook. Later on, you can make changes to the plan and make your own meal plans in accordance with your desired meal options.

Day #1

Breakfast: Eggs and Greens Breakfast Plate

Snack: Monkey Salad

Lunch: Poached Salmon

Dinner: Greek Salad

Day #2

Breakfast: Creamy Blueberry Breakfast Bowl

Snack: Chocolate Chip No Flour Cake

Lunch: Turkey Burgers

Dinner: Chicken Balance Bowl

Day #3

Breakfast: Whole30 Egg Toasts

Snack: Kale Chips

Lunch: Beef and Potato Bake

Dinner: Mediterranean Beef Salad

Day #4

Breakfast: Whole30 Breakfast Casserole

Snack: Fruit Cream

Lunch: Pesto Chicken

Dinner: Cauliflower Rice

Day #5

Breakfast: Protein Breakfast Salad

Snack: Broccoli and Potato Vinegar Salad

Lunch: Prosciutto Pork Wrap

Dinner: Sweet Potato Pasta

Day #6

Breakfast: Spinach and Brussel Sprout Eggs

Snack: Trail Mix and Coconut Yoghurt

Lunch: Tomato Soup

Dinner: Mustard Chicken with Garlic

Day #7

Breakfast: Apple and Squash Porridge

Snack: Faux Avocado Sushi Bites

Lunch: Mushrooms and Coconut Chicken

Dinner: Zucchini Noodles

Day #8

Breakfast: No Grain Oatmeal

Snack: Peach Mini Cobbler

Lunch: Greek One Pan Lunch

Dinner: Orange Chicken

Day #9

Breakfast: Korean eggs

Snack: Coconut and Berry Jar Cake

Lunch: Brussel Sprout Bacon and Apple Roast

Dinner: Mushroom Bowl with Cauliflower Rice

Day #10

Breakfast: Whole30 Burrito

Snack: Spicy Roasted Nuts

Lunch: Taco Soup

Dinner: Steakhouse Salad

Day #11

Breakfast: Potato and Zucchini Bake

Snack: Apple Cinnamon Pie

Lunch: Whole30 Sloppy Joe's

Dinner: Mini Pizzas

Day #12

Breakfast: Poached eggs

Snack: Banana Bread

Lunch: Cajun Style Shrimp Wraps

Dinner: Egg role in a Bowl

Day #13

Breakfast: Avocado and Bacon Whole30 Sandwiches

Snack: Stuffed Eggs

Lunch: Carrots and Chicken Roast

Dinner: Detox Salad

Day #14

Breakfast: Eggs Benedict with Asparagus

Snack: Sweet Potato Fries

Lunch: Beef Skillet with Sweet Potatoes and Zucchinis

Dinner: Baked Squash Spaghetti with Chicken

NOTE: You can change and adapt the meal plan in accordance with what you want to eat on the given day as long as all meals are Whole30 compliant.

CPSIA information can be obtained
at www.ICGtesting.com
Printed in the USA
LVHW051910280721
693919LV00005B/198